Down The Hill

A True Story Of Early Logging
In The Pacific Northwest

Roy E. Stier

BookPartners, Inc.
Wilsonville, Oregon

BookPartners, Inc.
P. O. Box 922
Wilsonville, Oregon 97070

To

my father, Roy Stier, Sr., and

grandfather, Walter Stier,

who preceded me in the employ of the

St. Paul & Tacoma Lumber Company

Acknowledgements

It was a matter of good fortune that reports from the logging camps to the business office of St. Paul & Tacoma Lumber Company were preserved by Corydon Wagner. They were made available from the archives of the University of Washington Library, together with original operational maps.

References to incidences of logging and camp life were enhanced by the recollections of Allan Malcom, Dave Voss, Mary Rummel and W. D. Hagenstein. My close association with Henry Beane was most helpful in the compilation of anecdotal notations.

Thanks to my wife Phyllis, whose constant encouragement and research assistance made it possible to see this book through to completion.

Table of Contents

Illustrations

Good Timber

The tree that never had to fight
For sun and sky and air and light,
That stood out in the open alain
And always got its share of rain,
Never became a forest king
But lived and died a scrubby thing.

The man who never had to toil
To rise above the common soil,
Who never had to win his share
Of sun and sky and light and air,
Never became a manly man
But lived and died as he began.

Good timber does not grow in ease:
The stronger the wind, the tougher the trees,
The farther sky, the greater length,
The more the storm, the more the strength;
By sun and cold, by rains and snows,
In tree or man good timber grows.

Where thickest stands the forest growth
We find the patriarchs of both,
And they hold converse with the stars
Whose broken branches show the scars
Of many winds and much of strife —
This is the common law of life.

– Author unknown; first printed by
– Kane & Harcus Co., Everett, Washington

The Day Of The Lumberjack

Since time, as we know it, is experienced as a period of passing events, the early settlers who came to America found wonders with which they dealt in the framework of a new "logging" culture, one they invented. The loggers were largely North Europeans and the environment they discovered was somewhat similar to their homeland, although different in tree species and physical features. Rivers and streams were untamed, transportation was difficult, flora and fauna was confusing, and environmental problems made homemaking a challenge.

The first tree cutting in America, other than the ship spars that were marked with the royal taboo, was for firewood and the building of homes and enclosures. Commercial cutting of forests came later, when there was a demand for the sawn products. Early pioneers of the woodlands had to develop new methods of cutting and milling, even a new language to express themselves in a new milieu. It was the beginning of a new breed of men and women. They were destined to expand their particular talents as far as practical parameters would permit.

Some controversy exists as to when and where the first sawmill was operational in the new world. From sifting through all the old documents, historians have concluded that it was not in Plymouth Colony, but in the town of York, Maine around 1623. This and other mills that followed were water-powered and used an old style upright saw in a frame driven by a connecting rod. Logs were moved against the saw by a pawl and ratchet gear. Strangely enough, this reciprocating sash saw idea is still used today with multiple saw blades. It is called a Swede Gang.

Even in those days the spirit of conservation prevailed. In 1640 the town of Exeter, now in New Hampshire, ordered that

"none shall fell any oke timber within half a mile of this part of the town except it be upon their planting lott, or for buildings or fences, upon the penalty of each tree 5 shillings."

The early logging season in Maine and New Hampshire lasted only 24 to 28 weeks, depending upon the weather. The "choppers" (saws did not make their appearance until the 1680s) began early in the fall and had to finish by January. Oxen were used to pull bobsleds to distant landings, which could be located several miles from the chopping site. Later horses were used because they were more mobile and cheaper to maintain. The sequence of change was repeated many years later in the far west.

Logs were often barked to facilitate moving and were nearly always sniped to keep them from digging in. On slopes the bobsleds had to be snubbed by wrapping the lines around a high stump. The horses often broke away when a snubbing line failed and they felt the slack. More often than not the animals were able to avoid being injured by a runaway sled. Oxen, however, being sluggish in movement, often were victims.

Early camps were quite crude and run by a "keeper" who supplied much of the food through his hunting and fishing prowess. Otherwise it was a diet of salt pork, beans, bread and molasses for the loggers. A keeper's pay for the season ran somewhere between $50 and $100, depending upon the size of the camp and the generosity of the owner. The bunkhouses were always smelly places, as drying clothes and shoes were both underfoot and hung on lines strung from ceiling hangers. The bunkhouses were built of logs with chinking of moss or mud, which allowed the cold wind to enter in many places. The early bunks were simply parallel poles filled with boughs or hay.

Many of the loggers were of French Canadian descent and they brought a familiar song with them called Alouette. It was sung with a great deal of gusto and enhanced with foot stomping. Some of the loggers came from Prince Edward Island and were called "P.E.Is." The natives used to make fun of them in a song which reflected their Scottish background. It went like this:

Oh, the boys of the island they are discontent,

For it's hard times at home and they can't make a cent,

So says Rory to Angus, "Here we're doing no good,

Let's go over to Bangor and work in the wood."

As the available timber was found farther and farther from the landings, another method of transportation had to be developed. This led to driving of logs down river to a more permanent sawmill location. Loggers found early on that cutting trees was much easier in the spring and summer months. When winter came the snow proved to be a friendly phenomenon as sled tracks were either naturally available or could be created with the addition of water, which froze in a short time. Obviously, river traffic came to a standstill in winter and logs had to be stockpiled.

River rafters were both a hardy and a foolhardy lot, who performed the most dangerous of all logging and lumbering jobs. Most of them were drawn from the logger groups who did their cutting in the warmer months and then the skidding to the river banks before high-water time. The logs had to be branded for identification and then pushed into the water when the time was right. Many of them solved the problem of how to keep from growing old by driving logs down hazardous white water, wild enough to capsize and drown them.

All went well as long as the logs were floating free, but log jams formed on nearly every bend of the river. Most of the "tenders" were stationed at these points and did their best to keep everything moving with poles and peaveys. Breaking a log jam was the epitome of heroism and called for a celebration with the survivor(s) being lionized as the best of the white-water men.

It was during these days that the loggers developed the caulked boot (later usually referred to as the cork shoe) in order to jump safely from log to log, trying to find the "king" or key log that had to be freed up to release the backup jam. Most of the river fatalities occurred when, after prodding, the logs finally did break loose, often trapping a logger in a gusher of wood and water.

Down river the logs were poled over to the mill site and rolled onto a jack ladder, a chain drive that brought them into the mill proper. Many of the loggers worked in the mill, as well as on the river. It was common to use the generic term "jack" (for jack of all trades) to apply to these workmen who wore several hats. It was a natural semantic progression to dub these hardy and versatile folks "lumber-jacks."

One of the most undesirable jobs in the early logging camps was that of the road icer. Since the winter nights were exceedingly cold it became the lot of one logger to drive a sprinkler wagon down the skid roads to the river or landing during the wee hours of the early morning. Each time he drove his team down the skid road he released a layer of water, which quickly froze in place. By morning the glare ice formed an ideal surface to sled logs, sometimes only a pair of horses needed to bring in a heavy turn.

Sunday was the only day off for the camp lumber-jacks. After working ten to twelve hours a day for six days they were happy to lay around the bunkhouse and do such odd jobs as resharpening or rehandling their chopping axes. Some of them played cards and usually used tobacco as the betting medium. Payday was normally once a month (sometimes at the end of the cutting season); by the time they returned from a gambling or debauchery spree in town most of them were broke.

Visitors to camp were a distinct novelty because of the usual access by trail only. Hardy salesmen sometimes made it to camp after a pay period, some of whom were enter-tainers as well in order to enhance their chances of making better deals. During the winter months at least one preacher would make it into camp. The loggers lack of piety did not preclude a warm welcome, however, because they were starved for company of any sort. A place on the long bench running the length of the bunkhouse was cleared for the sermon. The bench came to be known as the "deacon seat." This title persisted in all the bunkhouses of the west until the 1890s.

It was in the bunkhouse that tales of deeds were told and retold of the hardiest of the lumberjacks. Usually the exaggerations described the numerous fights that occurred in town. Prodigious strength was attributed to a few of the fanciful characters who could fall a tree faster or yard more logs to the landing than anybody else. Those tales that held the most interest developed a life of their own and prompted the poets of the time to perpetuate their memory.

The term "lumberjack" persisted as the logging areas moved westward into Wisconsin, Michigan and Minnesota, where many of the workers did indeed work both ends of the woods and milling operations. In the big timber migration to the far West it was again a new breed who handled the challenge of moving the gigantic trees to market. This became an age of specialization in which loggers, loaders, railroad men and millwrights were divided into even more diverse groups. For instance, each logging camp had its own push, side rod, rigging slinger, bull or donkey puncher, hook tender, bull bucker, busheler, whistle punk, cookee, flunkey, bullcook, etc. Only a greenhorn would let himself be called a lumberjack. However, the term persisted with some writers and in the media.

The Forest Primeval

Without a doubt some of the finest stands of Douglas fir, Western hemlock, Western red cedar and the Abies firs were found on the western slopes of Mt. Rainier. Homesteaders poured in during the 1880s to prove up on the even numbered sections in order to take advantage of their valuable timber assets. In early Pierce County records, no fewer than 70 aspirants were listed as vying for land in the prime township, the one east and south of Lake Kapowsin (then called Lake Kapousen).

This pressure on one particular area sparked a great deal of controversy, where claims for many parcels were listed as "in dispute." Some doubts existed as to the accuracy of the survey, which prompted the cadastral engineer's office to send one of its best surveyors out to establish official corners and section lines. Byron C. Majors commenced this important survey in September of 1890 and completed it in a little over two months. He did, indeed, find that some of the settlers' clearings encroached on their neighbors' claims, some mistakenly locating in odd-numbered sections.

Back in 1890 there was a small railroad station on the Puyallup River just north of Lake Kapowsin. Two of the earliest settlers, David Brown and John Chamberlain, combined efforts to build a five mile wagon road into the best of the timber lands from the station in a southerly direction where they and others fanned out to establish claims. Sections 16 and 36 were set aside in all townships for state stewardship, locally called school lands. The odd sections reverted to the Northern Pacific Railway Company as part of the corridor set aside to help compensate for the costs attendant to the completion of the main line into Tacoma.

Although the survey by Majors was an accurate one for its day, the method still in use for measurements was the old chain with actual links and a standard compass. A chain was 66 feet long with 100 links, so that measurements could be made to the nearest hundredth, albeit this apparent accuracy would later be declared relatively insignificant. In an attempt to correct for local compass needle deflections, surveyors did use sightings on Polaris from time to time. Typically, in Major's entry of the transcript he would write: "I therefore, sight on Polaris and leave the instrument in position till morning." One can only wonder what would happen if the instrument had been disturbed by heavy wind or animals during the night.

The original surveyors were required to set a post or

monument at 40 chains (1/2 mile) and at 80 chains for the full mile. During the progress along the section line they were to blaze trees with an axe on two sides, face on for those on the line itself, with quartering blazes for those near the line on either side. The scars from these axe marks were plain to see for many years after the fact and made it easy for timber cruisers and others to follow.

The pattern for the actual survey was to start at the previously marked southwest corner of the township, then progress eastward for six miles to establish the southeast corner. The line north from the latter was then run and by progressing basically west, with intermediate steps to fill in the blanks, the west line of the township was determined.

A strange anomaly was discovered in one of the townships in the Kapowsin area which was surveyed in the late 1890s. It was an obvious mistake, which was apparently accepted as a fait accompli because of a completion of the area surrounding it. It was discovered, but no correction was made, that a particular crew had dropped twenty chains (probably on an overnight stopover) on the south base line and did not discover the error until making the final closing on the west boundary of the township several weeks later.

Being under contract and standing to lose everything on a close margin wage scale, the crew evidently opted to carry out a deception to cover up their error. In any event they took the contract for the township to the north and gradually squeezed the left tier of sections together until they were back to the normal 80 chains in width. To this day, the west side of Township 18 North, Range 6 East, Willamette Meridian is "whopper jawed." Luckily no home-steading was done in this township, and when the deception was discovered by timber cruisers, it was apparently hushed up by an embarrassed government agency.

Forest lands destined for the St. Paul & Tacoma Lumber Company were characterized by deep glaciation from the rivers emanating at the base of Mt. Rainier. Originally called Mt. Takhoma (the mountain that was God), the mountain's Indian name was Anglicized to Tacoma. Later it was renamed Rainier after an English naval officer who observed the mountain from his ship in Puget Sound. He never came close to the peak that was to bear his name.

The gentle slopes running west from Mt. Rainier formed ideal soil conditions for the growth of the large trees that were discovered by the early pioneers. From the alpine firs near the timber line of the mountain to the great rift running nearly south along a string of lakes, a nearly unbroken canopy of valuable forest species existed.

Access to the area in the 1880s was by wagon road and trail from the village of Orting or by the same means from a small network of railroad tracks called the Tanwax & Western Railway. The projected rail line, which later developed into the Tacoma and Eastern, did follow the rift down the western side of Lake Kapowsin and Ohop Lake to the Nisqually River. A small station was maintained between the lakes, which became known as Ohop, later to become abandoned and grown over. For some years it was the only local post office for miles around and serviced the early logging operations in the area.

On the early cadastral engineer's maps, landmarks were given names used by the settlers who first arrived. One of the major lakes, first called Hemlock Lake, later became known as Clear Lake. Lake Doubtful was later named after its primary owner, F.D. Morgan. Several of the larger creeks were renamed after the first maps were released. Bradley Creek became Fox Creek and Boise Creek became Voights

Creek, the latter after an early developer who settled in its outfall.

One name change was brought about by a misinterpretation of the original survey notes. Tanwax Lake should have been Tanwat Lake. The error was made from a reading of the transcript of the original notes written by a person who crossed his t's with a downward angled slash mark, resembling an "x." The author found the original copy in the archives at Olympia, Washington, which clearly indicated that the intended name was Tanwat.

Timber cruisers were employed soon after the original surveys were completed so that long-range logging plans could be developed. Cruisers were really estimators of volumes by species for a specified area and had to be woods wise in order to ply their trade. They almost always worked with just one man, a compassman, who kept a cardinal direction and paced out the distance as he went.

Most cruisers were employed to sample the volume of trees in a stand of timber, say up to 25 percent, then apply that to the entire area for purposes of estimating the yield in board feet to be expected when logged. Some of these men were excellent topographers, whose maps of an area covered proved to be valuable to timber operators. C.A. Billings was one of those who turned out a finished product that was a credit to his profession.

Foresters have a name for the ultimate makeup of a stand of timber left to its own devises — a climax forest. As the tallest trees become dominant, the understory survives only to the extent that it has available light. The giants eventually fall as a result of nature's forces and are replaced by those able to stay in competition. The climax forest, therefore, is whatever remains at any given time, fulfilling the Darwinian principle.

While those of intellectual persuasion ponder the conundrum of whether sound is demonstrable when a tree falls in the forest beyond earshot, the trees do, in fact, continue to fall. This is the way of the forest primeval where things are in a sort of steady state as wind, lightning, floods, insects, fungus, beavers and other assorted phenomena are seeing to it that what is growing at one end is dropping off at the other.

Those who deplore the cutting of old growth seldom understand the magnitude of renewed forest areas, demonstrating a "dog in the manger" attitude toward those who would put it to wise use. In my youth, I made the trek around Mt. Rainier on the Wonderland Trail, where one could enjoy mile after mile of dense forest and alpine meadow. Then, as now, one would meet only an occasional person, and could wander fewer than 100 feet from the trail and observe trees that no other human had ever seen. When the Olympic National Park was set aside in 1938, it was suggested by one statistical expert that every man, woman and child in the United States could be placed in the public trust forests of the State of Washington so that no person could ever see another.

From Genesis To Fruition

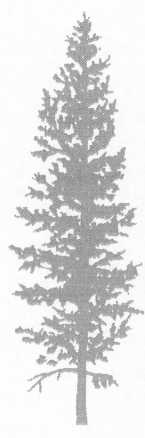

It was a series of events, many improbable, that coalesced to sow the seeds of opportunity into a favorable place among the emerging major lumber companies of the Pacific Northwest. In 1887 Colonel Chauncy Griggs passed through Tacoma, Washington on his way to an Alaskan visit and admired the vast stands of timber near Mt. Rainier. On his return to St. Paul, Minnesota he talked in glowing terms to his partner, Addison G. Foster, about the opportunities in the Puget Sound area. Later, when the partners were invited by a Northern Pacific Railway Company representative, they accepted a chance to visit the forest lands of the Northwest. They were hosted by T. F. Oakes, executive vice president of the company, and greeted by the new owner, Paul Schulze, upon their arrival in Tacoma. The story of the events preceding this meeting and what it portended for the future of logging in the Northwest is a compelling one; it deals with the many pitfalls that had to be surmounted before the establishment of the St. Paul & Tacoma Lumber Company.

Back in 1853, President Millard Fillmore signed a bill creating the Washington Territory which, at that time, included what is now parts of the States of Idaho and Wyoming. He then appointed Isaac Stevens as territorial governor. Stevens was a recently retired major in the army, who had distinguished himself in the Mexican War of 1846. Actually, it was the Major's experience as an engineer and his abounding interest in promoting a rail link with the Midwest that prompted his selection.

Governor Stevens had made a series of Indian treaties in an attempt to ameliorate some difficult situations between the tribes and the army under General John E. Wood. The latter became his adversary and teamed up with Secretary of War Jefferson Davis to block the Steven's plan to bring a railroad link through the Cascade Mountains into the Puget Sound area. Their efforts were stymied by the intervention of senators from Minnesota and Wisconsin, who were able to carry the day and pave the financial and legal way for a generous land grant to be established to aid in the railroad construction. Unfortunately, Isaac Stevens returned to the army during the last days of the Civil War and lost his life in the process, never realizing his dream of completing the Cascade route to Puget Sound.

Congress paused long enough during the Civil War to set up the necessary land grants enabling legislation that would lead to a charter for what was to become the

Northern Pacific Railway Company. The noted financier Jay Cooke took up the task of selling bonds in 1869, as he advertised the new Washington Territory as an area having an unusually mild climate with gigantic trees and rich lands capable of growing warm weather crops. The Jay Cooke Company soon raised $30,000,000 in the Midwest and an even a larger sum in Paris. The French deal fell through at the start of the Franco-Prussian War but plans for building the railroad were underway nevertheless.

Enter one Henry Villard, born in Baden, Germany as Ferdinand Heinrich Gustav Hilgard. His stormy early days as a university student organizing others against the government made life too difficult for him in his native country, and he emigrated to the United States. Fearing reprisals even at this distance, he adopted the surname of a French friend, hence the emergence of Henry Villard as the primary organizer for the railroad project. Henry invested his entire fortune in Northern Pacific stock, then came up with an idea to augment his holdings. He presented a scheme called a "Blind Pool" to drum up subscribers for his venture in a sort of substitute stock option. To his surprise, and to the surprise of many others, the seeking sum of eight million dollars was oversubscribed by twelve million.

Villard then took control of the Northern Pacific, and with his private stock and the solid backing of the twenty million, once again renewed the building project for the remaining 900 miles of track. He departed from the norm and used mainly Chinese labor. All went well until the track builders reached the Cascades, where some nearly impassable physical features plagued the project, together with severe labor troubles and monetary shortfalls. Destiny was altered once again as Villard lost out in a power play and Paul Schulze took over control of the company.

The problem of an all-weather route to connect up with the western slope of the Cascade Range still existed and time was running out. It appeared that the earlier plan to establish a terminus in Portland, then build an access line north to the Puget Sound area, was the most expedient course of action.

Nelson Bennett, together with his brother, took a very risky contract to build a two mile tunnel through the Cascades and once again make the dream of the Tacoma terminus feasible. The story of the Stampede Tunnel with all its attendant setbacks, not the least of which were serious labor problems with 13 fatalities, has been told and retold.

Actually, the first train over the new route between St. Paul and Tacoma finally made the trip in the summer of 1886. A temporary system of switchbacks made it over the Stampede Pass while the tunnel was being constructed from both ends. The people of Tacoma celebrated this link up with what was described as a "rip staver" — all consummated with a population of 8,000 celebrating in a complement of nearly 40 saloons. The all-weather link was finally completed via the Stampede Tunnel in 1887, just days before the penalty clause in the performance contract was to take effect.

Thus it was that Chauncey Griggs and Addison Foster made the exploratory trip to Tacoma in January of 1888. By another favorable happenstance, the Northern Pacific had received the largest land grant in United States history — forty sections of land for every mile of track laid down. A meeting was arranged by T. F. Oakes, the partners host, between Henry Hewitt, Jr. of Wisconsin and Oakes' close friend Charles Jones. Perhaps the partners noted that Charles Jones had the facial contours and trimmed beard of a famed visage, that of "Buffalo Bill" Cody.

It was from this arranged meeting that four people of varied backgrounds found common ground. After further explorations concerning a possible mill site, rail rates, financing, etc., the four signed the necessary articles to form the St. Paul & Tacoma Lumber Company in June of that year. This bargain not only represented the merger of old and new backgrounds but it reflected the route of the Northern Pacific, which made it all possible, with 80,000 acres of railroad grant lands pledged to seal the creation of the new company.

Corporate officers selected were Colonel Griggs, president, Addison Foster, vice president, Henry Hewitt, Jr. treasurer and George Browne, secretary. The latter was named because of his affiliation with the Northern Pacific corporate family, thus assuring liaison between the two parties. Charles Jones, with his extensive milling background, became the building advisor for the new sawmill to be built on the mud flats near Commencement Bay. Later, Hewitt and Jones teamed up to draw plans and oversee the logging operations.

The first logs were brought to the mill in the early spring of 1889. They came from the lakes area south of Orting and were transported over the spur known as the Tanwax and Orting Railway with an interchange just South of the Puyallup River. By January of 1890 the company had built nearly ten miles of standard gauge railroad southward from the village of Orting under a contract with the Northern Pacific. The original agreement called for the St. Paul & Tacoma Lumber Company to build and maintain trackage all the way south to the Nisqually River. However, it was becoming apparent that the cost could be prohibitive and jeopardize the continuance of the logging operations.

In the fall of 1890 a new agreement was negotiated whereby the Northern Pacific would take over the company spur that had been operating as the Tacoma and Orting Railroad. The extension down the west side of Lake Kapowsin was abandoned in favor of a plan to extend company maintained railroad spurs into the Ohop Creek drainage to the east.

By this time, the St. Paul & Tacoma Lumber Company was running seven camps, six by contractors, and Camp Seven as company operated, located near what later became the town of Kapowsin. These were all relatively small operating camps, employing a total of 200 men. Contractor camps were a definite savings in overhead costs but were gradually eliminated in order to maintain more control. By 1895 company Camp Eight was established on the south side of the Puyallup River with plans to push farther east.

This was how it all started. When one considers all of the pitfalls involved, the unravelling of circumstances leading up to the formation and activation of a major timber and lumber company were fortuitous for the formation of a wood producer, which was to become a primary player, and an important influence in the maturation of the forest industries of the Pacific Northwest. In a very real sense, the drama of building the St. Paul & Tacoma Lumber Company was a model, a prototype, for other pioneering lumber giants of the era. Its enthusiastic leadership, boundless enthusiasm, its vast resources of uncut timber, and the magnetism of its raw enterprise, which drew a remarkable and legendary variety of woods workers, were qualities echoed in the formation of similar lumber ventures. Together they represented a robust frontier culture of unusual vigor and impact on the formation of lasting social and economic institutions in the Pacific Northwest.

That Was Then

St. Paul & Tacoma Lumber Company's first mill on the Tacoma tideflats went into production in April of 1889. Using a new style of band sawing, Mill-A was set up to cut primarily Douglas fir. The very large cedar logs found in the timbered areas were also of importance to the company. Log trains coming in on the Northern Pacific were simply unloaded by rolling them off flatbed cars directly into the log pond. Logs were then pike-poled onto the jack ladder and onto the timber deck, where they were rolled onto the saw carriage with peaveys. It was soon discovered that this arrangement was unsatisfactory and a small rod engine was employed to sort logs on individual cars for off-

A hoisting frame was used in the 1890s to elevate oxen so they could be shoed by farriers. Photo courtesy of the Oregon Historical Society.

loading into sorting ponds. This procedure made it possible to control the type and size of logs, overcoming the limited opportunity of doing so at the woods landings.

Scattered holdings to the South of Orting were cut out by 1894 and the company laid plans for developing the bulk of its holdings to the east running all the way to Rainier National Park, except for a three-mile strip of National Forest to the west of the park. This was the era of the oxen, when an eight-to-ten yoke team was the standard yarding method. An old record book, circa 1892, discovered in the St. Paul & Tacoma Lumber Company vault, listed all of the oxen by name, together with an accounting of their feed bill and camp disposition. Oxen were usually housed in temporary shelters called "wickiups" (later a term used for men and equipment).

The bull driver (usually called "puncher") was the top man in camp and received the highest rate on a modest pay scale. Swampers cleared out the skid-roads for the roaders (often called "monkeys") who cut skids of about ten feet in length that were partially buried in the ground. These skids, usually spaced about nine feet apart, eventually became depressed in the middle from the heavy friction of logs during the yarding operation. A skid greaser always preceded the team with a bucket of grease and a swab to keep the turn moving along.

The oxen bulls were never in the lead, but placed somewhere in the middle of a team where their inherent

Oxen, such as these in 1894, were yoked together to pull heavy logs over a skid road. Gradually, they were replaced by the more efficient donkey engines. Photo courtesy of University of Washington Libraries, Seattle.

balkiness was overcome by the pressure of animals fore and aft. But the bulls were key movers of heavy logs after they were prompted into action. Oxen had relatively thin hooves and had to be shod at regular intervals, usually by an itinerant blacksmith. This was not an easy task, as the animals had to be herded into a specialized, confined log frame and lifted up with a belly band to get their feet off the ground. The passing of oxen teams and their bull punchers first replaced by horses, then by small steam donkeys, made the rivalry intense between the old and the new loggers. One of the best Northwest poets, Dan McNeil, caught the spirit of the bull puncher's despair in a poem published in The Timberman on July, 1909:

Early motive force in the woods: 14 oxen pull string of logs. Bulls were always located in the middle of the team. Photo courtesy of University of Washington Libraries, Seattle.

The Lay Of The Last Bull Puncher

The sun shone clear on the dying year,
    As I strolled down the old skid road;
The maple leaves, in fantastic weaves
        Of riotous color glowed.
A pine squirrel swore at a scolding jay,
    In a fir's deep branches hid,
When I came on the form of an aged man
        Who sat on the edge of a skid.

His head was bowed in his toil-wore hands;
    His shoulders were stooped and round;
A battered old hat, near the ground where he sat
        Lay on the sodden ground.
The light breeze whirls the snow white curls
    Of his tangled crown of hair;
While the sobs that shook his aged frame
        Told a story of deep despair.

"Oh, why do you moan in the woods alone,
    My good old man?" said I;
"What sorrow or fear hath brought the tear
        To bedim your once keen eye?"

"Oh, I mourn for the time when in life's full prime
I was a bull puncher bold;
And many a load, down this same skid road
I hauled in the days of old."

"Then I was king of the whole woods crew,
And I ruled with an iron grip;
And never a slob on the whole d----d job
Dared give me any lip;
But now, alas! those days have passed —
There's no job for me here;
My bulls are killed, and my place is filled
By a donkey — engineer."

"Instead of my stately team of bulls
All stepping along so fine,
A greasy old engine toots and coughs
And hauls in the turn with a line.
So that's why I'm sad, but for you, my lad,
I'll sing of those days again —
Your heart seems true, so I'll tell to you
How we used to do it then."

His weary old frame stood erect and tall
His eyes flashed as of yore;
And with tottering steps and croaking voice
He drove his bulls once more.

"Back, Buck! G-e-e, Spot! Whoa Mose! Haw, Star!
Steady there, Red! Back, Bright!
Now! Wiggle your tails, you long-horned snails
Or we won't get in tonight."

"Get into your yokes, you lazy blokes,
Old Bill's on deck once more;
And every bull must scratch and pull,
As he never pulled before."
So with many strange oaths and hoarse commands,
He staggered along in his dream —
Till, loud and clear, from somewhere near
Came a donkey engine's scream.

Bill stopped; at the sight of his agonized face,
My heart stopped with pity bled;
And e'er I could reach his side, he fell
Across the skid road — dead.
We buried him there on the scene of his past,
His headstone an old fir stump,
With this epitaph scrawled: "Old Bill has hauled
His last turn down to the dump."

When it became evident that oxen were not going to
compete with horses for log yarding, the transition became
rather abrupt. Although oxen were more powerful in a static
start, horses were faster and more responsive to commands.
Horses were also more alert and quick to avoid danger when

Woodsmen congregated in the bunkhouse in off hours, many occupying "the deacon's bench," which, in this photo, ran in front of the bunks. Pictured is typical bunkhouse, circa 1890. Photo by Webster and Stevens, University of Washington Libraries, Seattle.

the load they were pulling started to move in its own way. Oxen, on the other hand, did not react to a runaway turn and were usually "sluiced" in the process. In any event, horses proved to be cheaper to maintain, and this alone became a determining factor.

When the single drum pot, or donkey with the vertical gypsy spool, came into use by the St. Paul & Tacoma Lumber Company after the turn of the century, horses were still used on much of the terrain.

As donkey engines gradually replaced horses for primary yarding, the animals still had a last stand. They were used to take the yarding line out to the choker setters until multiple drum donkeys made their way onto the scene. Visual signals were made by a flagman who waved his hat to give directions to the man on the spot. The old method of engaging a yarding line was for a man to wrap several loops around the gypsy spool, being agile enough to keep away from the line bight. This procedure proved to be both inadequate and dangerous when hangups occurred. The loggers solved the problem by employing a second line, a haulback, with signals made by a jerkwire connected to the donkey.

In this photo from 1900, a single-spool donkey engine is pictured with crew, of which the engineer is standing holding the yarding line. Photo courtesy of University of Washington Libraries, Seattle.

The man or boy on the woods end of the jerkwire was often called the "punk" because his job classification was the lowest on the pay scale. The punk gave one jerk on the yarding line as a signal to go ahead. Another single jerk was the signal to stop. Two jerks signalled the haulback to be engaged to bring the chokers back. Finally, three jerks was the signal to go ahead slowly. Later, when whistles were installed on the yarders, the name "whistle punk" was given to the man in the woods who controlled the hand-held electrical contact device. This method persisted for many years, until radio contacts were installed.

Back in the days of oxen and horses, logs had to be loaded onto railroad cars by parbuckling. This term described the action of rolling logs with a section of wire rope from underneath and around in bight form. "Jump up" skids were set on an incline angled to the horizontal height of the car. The logs were hauled up the skid so there was

Founders of the St. Paul & Tacoma Lumber Company: (left to right) Percy D. Norton, Col. C.W. Griggs, Charles H. Jones. Addison G. Foster and A.L. Boyle. From the author's collection.

very little actual lifting involved. Single tongs with a "Y" strap were used later to skid and lift the logs. Sometimes a single boom, but normally an A-frame with a block, was the control mechanism for this operation.

Wages back in 1892 were modest, even for the times. In the West Coast Lumberman of that year the generally adopted wage scales for Northwest logging camps, per day, were reported to be:

Horse teamster	$4.75	Loaders, second $2.75
Ox teamster.	$3.75	Skidders, head $3.00
Sawyers.	$2.60	Skidders, common $2.50
Choppers or fellers	$3.00	Hooktenders, head $3.00
Choppers, second	$2.75	Hooktenders, common . .$2.75
Barkers	$2.40	Greaser. $1.90
Swampers, head.	$2.40	Barnman. $1.90
Swampers, common.	$2.00	Blacksmith. $2.75
Loaders, head	$3.00	Cook $3.00
Cookee (Flunkey).	$2.10	

The cost to board a logger in camp was $5.00 per day, which the company paid. With difficult times, many independent loggers were bought out by the larger companies. In 1892, the going price for logs loaded onto cars was $3.50 per thousand board feet. Even without stumpage costs there were many attendant working costs, and the small independents, or gyppo loggers, could not compete. In the so-called panic of '93, and the lean years that followed, there was little development in the woods operations as companies struggled to survive. It was not until the late 1890s that increased demand for building materials started to bring more innovation and improved efficiency to logging.

With the passing of oxen and horse logging a different nomenclature emerged in the woods to accommodate the new language of steam powered machinery. All harvesting of trees was handled by the "fallers" and "buckers," the latter cutting the trees to lengths and usually working alone. Buckers were also referred to as "bushelers" because they were paid by the board feet of products cut. The term "choppers" no longer applied because the only chopping done was to cut out the V-shaped opening at the tree base known as the undercut. This cleared wood area determined the direction for the tree to fall.

The term "swamper," which used to identify those who cleared out skid roads or sometimes sniped the ends of logs to prevent them from digging in, no longer applied to the same job classification. Swampers became those who cleaned out around steam shovels and cleared right-of-way for railroading and landing sites.

Most of the other terms from the early days persisted in one form or another. The head loader, the man in charge at the landing for loading all logs, was usually referred to as the first loader. Second loaders (normally two at a landing) still were charged with setting the parbuckle line and later to place the tongs for loading logs onto the cars.

Hooktenders were the foremen of the crew that secured the chokers or wire rope straps around the logs to be yarded (any means for getting logs to the landing was referred to as yarding). The hooktender's crew consisted of two or three choker setters, who placed the sections of wire rope around the logs to be yarded, and the whistle punk, who did the signaling, early on by a jerk wire and later by an electronic device attached to a whistle.

From the days of the oxen and horses up to the large donkey machines, the operation of bringing the logs in had always been called "yarding." It was not until spar trees were fitted with blocks (pulleys) that yarding became an easier process because the "turn," or group of logs coming in to the landing, could be lifted up in front to prevent hangups. Animal yarding and the early donkeys, or pots, all used the "ground lead" technique that gave only minimum control against getting fouled up except in the case of the skid roads, where obstacles were removed.

High lead (later hi-lead) was the name given to any woods operation in which the logs were brought in to a spar tree or steel spar mounted on a modified railroad car. When the heavier third line was drawn tightly between the spar tree and a back spar or high stump at the far end, called a "skyline." A carriage (multiple block unit) ran on this static line and fed the chokers down to the hook tender, sometimes far below. There were many types of skylines used, however the logging method, dubbed "skidding," still applied for the most part.

To a more limited extent, a type of yarding called a "slack line" was employed. This system was rigged like a skyline but carried a heavier line (usually 2 inches in diameter) which could be raised or lowered to fit the topography and had its primary use for reaching into canyons. The use by Hollywood filmmakers of the term "skyline" was best exemplified when actor Fred McMurray, in a movie, carried in a haulback block and plunked it down on the forest ranger's desk. A haulback block on a skyline system could not be carried by any combination of men.

The days of bigger and bigger machinery with larger-diameter lines finally reached its limit under the primary law of diminishing returns. When labor costs mounted to a certain point new machinery was devised to meet the need. For instance, a wide-opening block called a Tommy Moore came into favor because it allowed the group of choker ends to pass through so that the turn could be loaded onto cars without stockpiling.

Two donkey engines, one for loading and one for yarding logs, chug away in a forest landing. Man in foreground gives dimension to machines and logs. About 1910. Photo courtesy of University of Washington Libraries, Seattle.

The Century Turns

One of the early camps operated by the St. Paul & Tacoma Lumber Company had no number or location name — it was simply called "rolling camp." Before the Northern Pacific took over the Tacoma and Orting Southern spur, the area around Orting Lake had an ideal log delivery terrain, a steep hillside nearly devoid of trees. Horses brought their turns to the brow of the hill and the logs were rolled down very near to the track below, hence the origin of the camp's name. Evidence of old skid roads with their high stumps fitted with snubbing spools were visible in this area many years later.

Early logging west of Lake Kapowsin culminated in the late

1890s, when the last spur built for the company by the Tacoma and Eastern Railroad ran eastward along the south side of the Puyallup River. Several contractors were still operating for St. Paul & Tacoma Lumber Company near the main line as the last company camp on the Puyallup spur, called Camp Eight, completed the logging in the flat that was to become the site for a power plant.

The area to the east of Lake Kapowsin had developed considerably after the turn of the century. The old Brown-Chamberlain road became the ward of the county, but the very ambitious project by the Puget Sound Power & Light Company was the primary subject of conversation with the locals.

The One-Spot early model shay (steam locomotive) chugging through timber about 1900. Photo by C. Kinsey, University of Washington Libraries, Seattle.

New style bunkhouses were introduced by the company in 1910. These are at the Buckley Camp site. From the author's collection.

Construction started in 1902, when a road was built up the steep hillside and along the brow of the hill on the south side of the Puyallup River. The power company cleared its own right-of-way and set up a small sawmill below the intake site to cut timbers for construction of the flume. A standard gauge track was laid down on the wooden conduit where the speeders and supply trailers could operate.

The main source of water supply was the river itself at a point called the headworks, located at the 1600 foot level. Since the glacier water was quite milky during several months of the year, two other clear streams were tapped to lower the colloidal content. Altogether, the builders constructed 10 1/4 miles of main flume line with a settling basin to remove the heavier particles. From the exit pond the drop via penstock was 871 feet, as five delivery tubes developed considerable force for the station's turbines below.

Completed in April of 1904, this power source is still operating at full capacity today. Through the years it became somewhat of a headache to the St. Paul & Tacoma Lumber Company as the flume line cut across much of the timber access and necessitated some major changes in logging plans. The last of the "old timers," centenarian Dave Voss, tells of a daring operation where he took a cold deck donkey over the top of the flume line in 1909 and down the treacherous slope to cross the Puyallup River. Years later C.E. Marek was not so lucky, as he was pinned under the wreckage of his donkey when the snubbing line broke.

With the extension of the Northern Pacific spur down the east side of Lake Kapowsin it became evident that a large and more permanent camp was needed. This became known as Kapowsin Camp, built for family use, and with the purchase of several miles of 56-pound steel, (steel is rated by the weight per yard), it started the push into the main location of the 80,000-acre railroad grant lands. Jack Murphy, a stocky Irishman, was named camp foreman after he completed his stint at Camp Eight.

An all-Italian track gang worked out of the new camp as they started laying steel up the Ohop Creek drainage basin. Engine Number Two, with John McKay at the throttle, was the first of the new generation of heavier shays to work out of the Kapowsin Camp. Later this locomotive became known as the Two-spot. It was destined to outlast all the rest of the company fleet and became a sort of sentimental favorite with the local engineers.

As an adjunct to camp life, several locals established a saloon on the small island near the bunkhouses. Within a short time, it was expanded into an operation in which some of the ladies engaged in the "oldest profession," and was known as the Bluebird. A narrow wooden walkway with a handrail on one side was the sole access across the lake except by boat. Tales from the bunkhouses in later years recount the demise of several loggers who did not make it back and were later found in the lake. These were usually the unmarried ones who chanced the crossing in a drunken state. Obviously, the camp wives took a dismal view of their spouses being exposed to this sort of debauchery.

Meanwhile, the St. Paul & Tacoma Lumber Company had logged out the Crocker Hill area east of Orting and established the second of the bigger camps in Township 19 North, Range 6 East. This was known as Buckley Camp and was basically built to salvage the fire-killed timber from the great burns of 1902. Both Kapowsin and Buckley camps were considered all-weather. However, the big snows of January, 1908 closed them down for more than a month.

W. B. "Bush" Osborne (1919) in flying uniform standing by his DeHavilland (D.E H-9). Such observers performed important aerial forest surveys. Photo courtesy of the Oregon Historical Society.

Horses were still being used in the woods, mostly in place of a haulback line for the early yarding pots. On Crocker Hill the company experimented with a yarding method known as a "trailing road." This operation utilized a small gear engine to pull logs down between the rails to a landing some distance away. It was hard on the oversized ties (skids) and required special heavy-duty spools to navigate the curves, hence it was not used anywhere else.

Log loading was still being done on some sides by the old parbuckling method as the company resisted using the innovative McLean loading boom, which other companies had already installed. Part of the reluctance to the conversion was due to the skill of two men — Anton Wickman, the leading single tong man, and Fred Woolery, a donkey engineer with an expert's touch. They were acclaimed as icon equivalents in the brotherhood of log loaders.

Living conditions in the camps had not improved much since the days of the three decker bunks. A logger's seniority was signalled as he worked his way down from the top bunk to the most preferable, bottom one. Some of the loggers still carried their own bed rolls, called crummies, in which most of their possessions were rolled up. Back in 1908 a poem written by a logging camp cook signing himself as "Doc Wilson" appeared in the Pacific Monthly. It was prompted by the demise of a whistle punk named Anderson who was brought to his bunk after being caught in the bight of the main line. It went like this:

The Bunkhouse

Oh bunks and bunks
Valises and trunks;
Blankets and swags by the score;
Smoky oil cans,
Old spittoon pans,
Scattered all over the floor!

Old gunny sacks
Filled from the stacks
Of hay in the field nearby;
Under your nose
Pillow your clothes,
And sleep with many a sigh.

Old broken door
Drags on the floor,
Overhead the nightbats hide;
The roof's too thin
And rain drips in
The bunk where Anderson died.

Old shirts and coats
Where spider gloats
On the flies and moths in his lair.
Rusty old stove,
Socks by the grove,
Polluting the room's warm air.

Off to the junks!
Bunkhouses and bunks!
For the toiler requires rest.
A clean, warm bed,
Or home instead,
And then his labors are blest.

At the national level lumber consumption was exceeding forty billion board feet per year, and at the same time (1904-1905), indictments were being served against timber groups and land speculators as they were charged with conspiracy and defrauding the United States in timber land dealings.

So it was that Gifford Pinchot, head of the federal forestry service, created large areas of National forests to ensure proper stewardship for the Western forest reserves. The high water mark of the court proceedings was called the "Oregon timber steal," all of which was far removed from the St. Paul & Tacoma Lumber Company, whose operations were many miles and considerable operating years away from forest service lands.

Bankruptcy proceedings with the Northern Pacific prompted the suicide of Paul Schulze and agreements with the St. Paul & Tacoma Lumber Company had to be reinterpreted. Percy Norton died unexpectedly and his position as assistant treasurer with the lumber company was filled by John Hewitt. Meanwhile, John's father, Henry Hewitt, was accumulating a considerable amount of forested land in Pierce County. This acquisition of timber lands later was converted to the Hewitt Land Company, where vast holdings were disposed of in piecemeal fashion throughout the earlier years of the 20th century.

Colonel Chauncey Griggs started his son, Everett G. Griggs, through the training program in the mill that culminated in his being named superintendent in 1893. Colonel Griggs named Everett to succeed him as president in 1908. The Colonel survived in poor health for only a few more years.

Certainly one of the greatest men to emerge on a national scale to serve in close association with the timber industry was Edward Tyson Allen, or E.T., as he was known to his many friends. His family homesteaded in 1889 at a location just a few miles south of the St. Paul & Tacoma Lumber Company's major timber holdings. Young Edward received a congressional appointment in 1898 to the United States Bureau of Forestry, attached to the Secretary of the Interior. Later as State Forester of California and then as District Forester for Washington, Oregon and Alaska, he carved out a most memorable name for himself.

I knew him only in the twilight of his life, as he liked to recall some of the incidents of his youth and the early legends that he enjoyed telling of the Polynesian culture. He and his wife took a sailing ship to Tahiti where he established a vanilla plantation in 1902. This successful venture was brought to a shuddering halt when the German cruiser Emden bombarded the plantation to rubble as a gesture of dominance during the early days of World War I.

During the interim years, he teamed up with Col. William Bukhout Greeley to form the Western Forestry and Conservation Association in 1909. It was at some of these meetings many years later that I had some long conversations with E.T. He would often say, "Why does a young fellow like you find an old man like me interesting?" It was not his many contributions to forestry in the public interest that was overwhelming, but his lucid accounts of early incidents with Gifford Pinchot and others during his travels that were so fascinating. Stewart Holbrook, in his article Prophet of Forestry, best described how unique this man was and how he profoundly affected all those who followed.

Down The Hill

The first known logger to enter the newly discovered Douglas fir forests of the Northwest was C.A. Bradbury in 1847. He came from York County in Maine and cut down his first big Douglas fir near the Columbia River in Oregon. The tree measured eight feet in diameter and he discovered that it was not just the large size that presented a problem, it was the large amount of pitch that flowed into the undercut. In a later discovery, he found that cutting at a higher level reduced the amount of pitch flow.

High stumps were common well into the 1920s, but not because of the pitch — it was to get away from the flare of the tree butt. Undercuts were normally chopped

Early fallers demonstrate the size of a giant Douglas fir by one of the crew installing himself in the perpendicular undercut. Note the spring boards and the 11-foot saw. Photo courtesy of University of Washington Libraries, Seattle.

out and then the tree cut from the back side with a two-man crosscut saw. This was heavy work and the saws were dubbed "misery harps," later on more commonly called "misery whips." The pitch problem was fairly well solved by coating the saw with kerosene or coal oil.

After solving the pitch problem these fallers from the eastern and midwestern forests had to come up with a way to contend with the natural flaring of the large tree butts. With some degree of intrepidity, they discovered a way to get off the ground far enough to circumvent the tougher root area, to where the diameter was more favorable. They "boarded up" to a height of ten to twelve feet with a series of notches cut progressively in a spiralling upward pattern. Spring boards were made of sturdy wood, approximately five feet in length and up to eight inches wide and tapered at both ends. One end was fitted with an angle iron that locked into the notches of the tree trunk. When a man's weight was on it, the board settled into a horizontal position and made a substantial platform for handling one end of a saw or for chopping the undercut.

The standard length of a crosscut saw for the big timber was nine feet. However, sometimes a special length was needed for those trees of excessive diameters. With a two-man falling set, a throw of up to 24 inches was needed in order to get the maximum cutting effect. If you were to check the tops of the larger diameter stumps a noticeable dishing effect is evident. This was caused by the weight of the saw gradually forming a concave configuration by force of gravity.

In the early days, most trees were felled toward a convenient direction, meaning down the slope in a typical hill country. Because of the amount of breakage, this practice gradually changed until there was a great deal of finesse in "gunning" a tree toward a more favorable direction, notably along the hillside or away from another stump, which would result in "spiking." Shattering a tree bole over a stump was deductible on the scaler's tab.

When a faller and his partner had just about completed the job of putting down a tree, they called out a warning to anyone who might be in the area. Although faller sets were placed well away from others by the bull bucker, accidents could happen and it was always a standard practice to "call" a tree going down. In my many years of experience in woods operations, coupled with information gleaned from others, the call of "timberrrr" has never been heard in the forests of the Northwest.

The standard call is "down the hill," but the call of "brush" is often used, particularly on flat areas. Sometimes the call can be "heads" as is common in the pine areas of Eastern Oregon. Sometimes the call is something quite unintelligible — something like a cross between the mating call of Bigfoot and the cry of an unlucky logger caught in a bear trap. In any event, a timely warning was used, but no self-respecting faller would ever cry out "timberrrr." To do so would have been a near heretic revelation that would have dogged the logger's days for a long time.

It was a common sight to see a faller line up his axe on the line of the undercut and use the handle as the direction for the tree to fall. Sometimes bets were made as to the ability of a faller to get his tree down in a tight squeeze. Those who were the most experienced could not only gun it but set up a little rotation to turn a tree in the falling process. They accomplished this trick by wedging or, if they were really top men, by canting the undercut to give a tree a little rotation when it started to fall.

Not all trees behaved as they should and so accidents did happen in spite of normal care. One of the worst hazards was the "widow maker," which could take the shape of a rotten limb, a heavy bark slab that came loose, an understory tree that bent in the falling process and snapped back when released, etc. A hangup of a tree that did not fall when cut usually caused the greatest hazard because it meant dropping another tree over it to put it down, with the result that there might be two possible bad actors to contend with. A hangup could also cause the tree to roll off in either direction or kick off the stump when released.

Another hazard attendant to the falling process was where the tree "barber chairs," instead of going down cleanly. This happened when the base of the tree split upward and peeled back some distance above the ground. This sort of thing, along with the less common kickback, was not predictable and meant split-second timing was

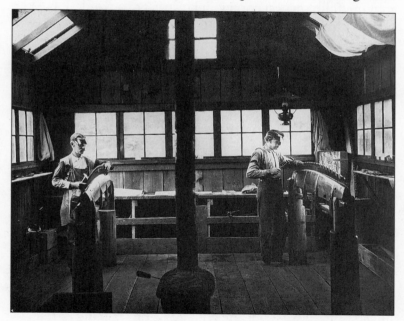

Saw filers plying their trade in a well-lighted shack. Small hammers were used to set the saw teeth at the proper angle. About 1900. Photo by C. Kinsey, University of Washington Libraries, Seattle.

required to avoid the grim reaper. The latter hazard was mainly on heavy leaners or when another tree was too close and sheared when going down.

Usually the bull bucker sent in a crew of windfall buckers to cut to length the sound down trees which had fallen fairly recently. This practice saved breakage when a standing tree fell because a log would tip upward when hit and cushion the tree going down, thereby preventing a possible shatter. Windfall buckers worked alone and normally had the job of swamping out an area to work and dig under where the cut was to be made.

One Monday morning back in the early 1940s, I was looking for a section corner and overheard a windfall bucker talking to himself. Since this was unusual behavior, I stopped to hear what his internal conversation was all about. It went something like this: "Hokay ya dumn Svede, so ya got tanked up and lost all yer money — hokay, so now ya pull this damn saw witout no oil!" I found out later that the bucker punished himself until noon by deliberately withholding oil from his saw, thereby increasing his labor. He finally oiled the surface when the sticking got too much for him.

After the falling was done in an area, usually out of range of any trees coming down, the "bushelers" moved in. These were the contract cutters who limbed the trees and cut them to regular log lengths. Sometimes this could be done to fill special orders, but normally the standard was 32 and 40 feet, with an additional foot or so to allow for squaring off and mill trimming. Before the days of peeler blocks there was not much stress on making strategic decisions. The bull bucker followed along after the bushelers and tallied the diameters and lengths of logs so that he could report the amount of volume for each one.

Fallers and buckers were paid on a piece-work basis, all of which made for some lively discussions as to area assignments.

As part of the passing parade, fallers and buckers of the crosscut saw era were a unique lot. They were not

The largest tree ever cut in the State of Washington — a Western red cedar. Photo courtesy of University of Washington Libraries, Seattle.

usually of large stature, but made up for bulk with a wiry constitution, well adapted to the endurance required for their chosen occupation. In the bunkhouse, they were men of few words, sitting for long periods of time with hands folded and staring at the floor, apparently reliving the events of the day and anticipating the prospects for the next. Although appearing to be stoic, they did reflect a natural respect for their fellow men and were generous to those in need, albeit not normally able to express their inner feelings.

Fallers going to the job were loaded down with their saw and spring board over their shoulder, a heavy canvas bag with wedges hanging on a shoulder strap and carrying a double bitted axe and heavy maul. Bushelers did not use spring boards but still had to use wedges to keep their saw running freely. Their axes had distinguishing parallel grooves on the handle which supported the back of the saw on cuts made from below. Both carried saw oil in a bottle fitted with a hook resembling a gaff, which was hung from the bark of a tree or log.

"Tin" pants were the order of the day, which always became stiffer with age as they soaked up tree sap, pitch and saw oil. I have seen some pants actually stand up by themselves in the corner of a bunkhouse. Nearly all had the telltale dark outline and impression of the ubiquitous snoose can that was carried in the back pocket. Like the donkey punchers, riggers, hook tenders and the rest, fallers wore the traditional black underwear. All of this went together with the day of the misery whip (or brier), where sheer human effort played such an important part in the forests of the big trees. Alas, their time on the stage of life is over and there is no curtain call.

Enter, The Shay

There is a certain fascination with steam locomotives that surfaces early among some boys and persists in later life. Following the development of locomotives from wood to coal burners, metamorphosing into diesels, has been an avocation for a good number of chroniclers. Loggers and lumbermen were foremost among those who experimented with special models for adaptation to the particular needs of the timber industry.

Strangely enough, the standard gauge, which was adopted by most timber operators to allow interchange with common carriers, was copied from the Roman chariots of 2000 years ago. Their wheel gauge was adapted to use the ruts in the stone roads of the day and common practice became the standard. It was as late as 1886, however, before the major railroads of the United States formally adopted the standard of four feet, eight and a half inches. Most of the railroads that used the so-called "narrow gauge" standardized on a spacing of an even three feet.

Wide gauge engines were constructed because it was felt that the wider distances between rails would provide extra stability and power. For instance, one locomotive which was only mildly successful was the "geared

Pictured is the Two-Spot engine pulling a load down the Camp One main line. Photo by C Kinsey, University of Washington Libraries, Seattle.

The Three-Spot brings a load of logs into Camp Six in 1927. Photo by C. Kinsey, University of Washington Libraries, Seattle.

monster," that operated north of Seattle in the early 1880s. It had an unheard of gauge of seven and one half feet. Special track and maintenance requirements precluded this oversized engine from becoming used beyond the experimental stage. Another innovation, also doomed to failure, was one that used a nine foot spacing between wheels. This monstrosity ran on wooden rails and had a predictable demise.

Locomotives for logging operations had to measure up to some fairly exacting demands. They had to be heavy enough to pull a number of cars, be able to navigate sharp curves, handle grades up to nine percent and be easy to maintain. The challenge was accepted by one Ephriam Shay, a lumberman from Michigan. His prototype was a strange looking affair with an upright boiler in the middle of a wooden frame, fitted with drive wheels fore and aft. He used wooden rails at first because they could be built for less than 800 dollars per mile.

Shay's first successful model hit the market in 1882 and sported a steel frame with two powerful cylinders and weighed nearly 15 tons. Later improvements, particularly for the timber trade, included the horizontal offset boiler and geared trucks on the right side, which became a familiar sight. Here was an engine with improved static pulling power that could handle adverse grades of over eight percent and had uniform exhaust to boot. There was no need for counterbalance because the stroke and recovery cycles were in perfect sequence.

Shay's closest competitor was the Climax, which was manufactured in Pennsylvania and was a little cheaper product than the Shay. Its late start in the market and its slower ability to adapt to particular demands prevented it from ever catching up. When the St. Paul & Tacoma

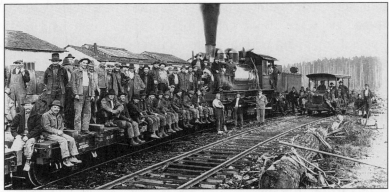

Black smoke from coal-fired Five-Spot Shay places an exclamation point to the gathering of the entire woods crew from Camp Three. The author rode on the small speeder on the passing track during his first visit to the camp in 1927. From the author's collection.

Here, the old style trestle construction supported the spur line that came into Camp Eight in 1926. From the author's collection.

Lumber Company first incorporated in 1888 there were 200 "sidewinders" (Shays) in the eastern woods, the year when the first Climax engine was sold.

Later models of the Climax, and the type that persisted until the company folded in 1928, had large cylinders inclined at 45 degrees on either side of a centered boiler. The crankshaft ran crosswise with the boiler center line and transmitted power to a central shaft through a master gear. They made quite a few with double-flanged wheels, but as the timber industry upgraded the quality of rails, they became obsolete.

Rated number three in popularity with loggers was the Heisler. Charles Heisler manufactured his first models in Erie, Pennsylvania and sold the first group in 1894. The two cylinders on his model formed a V to drive a shaft that ran down the middle of the boiler and had the innovation of oil seals. Again, this was a balanced engine and Heisler's advertising pointed out one defect of the Shay, which was its habit of wearing out the rails on the right side due to the pounding of the cylinders away from the offset boiler.

For many years the debate about the best gear engine was carried out in the Tacoma clubs, in local saloons and in the bunkhouses. The Climax had a simple design but probably was the least efficient. Heislers had a reputation for being poorly built, but had more direct power transferred to the drive shaft. Shays had exposed gears that made them vulnerable to damage. However, by the same token, they were more easily reached for repairs. Weyerhaeuser Timber Company played the percentages by investing in all three.

St. Paul & Tacoma Lumber Company standardized with Shays and at one time had nine of them in full service. They were numbered in sequence on the front end of the boiler within a circular frame. Since this design could be thought of as a "spot," each engine was referred to as the One-spot, Two-spot, etc. The first engine was an early model that proved too light and wore out prior to 1915. The Two- and Three-spots were the first of the heavier and improved models that survived to the end of the railroad era.

When I first visited the shops at Camp One in 1929, the Four-spot was being cannibalized for parts. It had had a boiler accident in which the crown sheet dropped and made repairs unfeasible. The Three-spot was inactive in the late 1920s, but later was rebuilt to haul center-dump gravel cars for track ballasting. As the amount of main line and spur track increased, a need for rod engines on the long haul became evident. The Seven-spot and the Ten-spot were purchased as a result. Products of the Baldwin Locomotive Works, they were saddle tank Mallets that ran from camp sidings to the interchange with the Northern Pacific

Railway Company. Except for a short time in 1926 when the Seven-spot was overhauled, they were in continuous service.

The last Shay in the gear engine group was purchased from Clear Lake Logging Company when it shut down operations in the early 1930s. The 11-spot was taken to the Nooksack operation in Whatcom County, but returned to the main operation in April of 1933. The 12-spot became the most reliable of the Shays and survived to pull the last train load of logs out of the woods.

When Dempsey Lumber Company started up logging operations near Camp One in late 1930 it made arrangements to use existing St. Paul & Tacoma Lumber Company tracks. Jim Dempsey bought two Heislers for his timber operations and enough steel to run spurs into his holdings in the Ohop Creek drainage areas. An eight year contract provided for the hauling of ballast at the rate of 10 cents per mile, per car. An interchange was developed at Camp One, where a charge of $7.00 per car was negotiated to deliver logs to the Northern Pacific Kapowsin spur, where they were picked up for delivery to the Dempsey sawmill in Tacoma.

Dempsey Lumber Company completed logging in the Camp One area within its contract time of eight years and did not need to execute the two year extension proviso. Our good relationship paid dividends when we were able to acquire the Dempsey properties in 1942 as an excellent addition to the new tree farm program. Since most of the Dempsey holdings were previously settled by homesteaders, all of these areas had a sizeable stand of second growth from the 1880 to 1890 clearings. These strategically located stands seeded the surrounding St. Paul & Tacoma Lumber Company properties as they were logged off.

Another somewhat symbiotic relationship was developed with the Buckley Lumber Company when St. Paul & Tacoma Lumber Company needed to get back into the White River Gorge to salvage timber to be flooded by the proposed Mud Mountain Dam. Our old camp in the area was closed in 1910 when nearly all the timberlands were logged off. This camp was first opened after the turn of the century and was nearly burned out in the rash of fires of September, 1902.

An agreement was made with Buckley Lumber Company to take over the primary steel rails as they pushed farther eastward into their last holdings. Years later when we needed to get back into this area for the scattered timber threatened by the dam on the White River, Buckley Lumber Company was just about on its last legs. As a result, the company's track was in a shambles and only one old Climax locomotive remained. It was a hair-raising experience to ride their speeder down the track, rocking from side to side, a five mile stretch patched with Dutchmen and barely maintained with sparse ballast. Needless to say, we all felt that a celebration was in order when we completed the logging operation without a serious casualty.

The Shadow Of
War Clouds

Archduke Francis Ferdinand
was not a name many loggers knew.
They were not alone in this respect,
as only a handful of people ever
knew of the players in world power
politics. In any event, the Austria-
Hungary principals tagged the Serbs
as the heavies in an act of violence
and the fat was in the fire.

The year 1914 was pretty
much status quo for the St. Paul &
Tacoma Lumber Company, as the
war to end all wars had not reached
the timber industry except to increase
anxiety. Interchange with the
Northern Pacific had been established at the old Kapowsin Camp
site. It was six years before the first
logs would be dumped into Lake
Kapowsin and sorting would become

more crucial. Camp One was running several sides and had pushed the railroad into Little Ohop Creek where the new Camp Three was to be built.

Camp Two was accessible by county road with the junction just below the camp buildings. It was to be later known as Bootlegger Crossing when the 18th amendment threatened to constrict one of the logger's favorite pastimes. Beyond Camp Two, a construction camp was set up near Wade Creek, which later became Camp Four, or more often called "Ladysville" by the loggers and natives. It was the first company camp to hire female flunkeys and was the place where E.W. Allison started his long career with the company.

Meanwhile, the war in Europe was proving to be a protracted affair and air power was starting to play an important role. First, in observation later, in strafing and bombing. The light planes in use required stringers and cross members of strong, light wood, which fit the specifications of Sitka spruce. This species grew fairly large in parts of western British Columbia and Washington. The popular British S.E.5 and S.E.5a, together with the French Nieuport 28c, used considerable amounts of this wood, when available. The early S.P.A.D., first produced in 1913, developed a need also as production of the 1916-1917 models was pushed to the limit.

To meet this increasing demand for Sitka spruce, the United States set up a private cooperative, the Spruce Production Corporation, with the War Department handling the logistics and furnishing most of the manpower. Col. Bruce E. Disque (later promoted to general), headed up this shared effort mostly with recruits. The effort was logically dubbed the Spruce Division. It was then that another person was to emerge in a claim to fame, caught up in the spruce rage. The name of W. E. Boeing appeared on many section plats in Grays Harbor County. He first invested in forest land, followed by actual construction of aircraft. The rest of the story is well known.

When it became clear that the United States would be drawn into the war, a group of lumbermen met to coordinate their efforts in planning for the cantonments that would be needed for an expeditionary force. They elected W. B. Greeley as secretary, however, it was soon evident that he was the man to implement these plans on site near the front lines. The 10th Engineers, American Expeditionary Force, was created with Greeley in command.

Col. Greeley emerged as the leader of 20,000 engineers, who manned the forest and milling operations for the allied war effort. Some troops were engaged in cutting piling, telephone poles and fuel wood. This large contingent was formally called the Forestry Division of the American Service of Supply, ending up delivering over six hundred million board feet of sawn lumber to the American sector. By the end of the war in 1918, Col. Greeley was managing 90 sawmills, scattered over all the forests of France.

Rearing its ugly head to take advantage of increased production and diminished regulation, was the organization known as the Wobblies, or International Workers of the World (I.W.W.). They were pledged to organize against what they perceived to be employer excesses in all fields of labor. In particular, they were intent upon destroying capitalism. With a big bang entry into contention, the Wobblies had dynamited the ex-governor of Idaho in 1905. By 1907, some of the organizers were sporting badges on which was printed "I am an undesirable citizen!"

Loggers and sawmill workers had been very independent, but inroads by the I.W.W. caused many shutdowns in

1907 as part of the organizational drive. For the next decade, the pressure generated by them gave the lumber industry fits. It culminated on November 5, 1916 with what was called the "Everett Massacre." Nearly 400 members chartered a ship in Seattle and docked in Everett where they proceeded to shoot up the waterfront area, leaving seven dead and 68 wounded.

With America's entry into the war soon after the Everett Massacre, the Wobblies staged the greatest strike in lumber history.Eighty-five percent of the camps were shut down, but the felonies were played out in train derailments, arson, spiked logs, etc. Camp and mill crews tried fighting back, but they were outmaneuvered and the courts seemed unable to bring enough to justice to make a dent in lawlessness.

It was the Spruce Division to the rescue under the leadership of General Disque. They formed a counter organization in the form of the Loyal Legion of Loggers and Lumbermen, known by all as the 4Ls. It was built on the idea of equal representation between employers and workers. They negotiated an eight hour day, improved living conditions in the camps and adjusted wages to fair levels.

While the negotiations were going on, all the men went back to work, thus foiling the Wobblies and depriving them and their "plug uglies" from terrorizing the industry. The Wobblies continued to wield some power after the war, but not in the timber industry. They were able to call a general strike in 1919, but as the prisons were finally closing their doors on the organizers, all activity slowly ceased. I.W.W. general secretary, Big Bill Haywood, was able to escape the country and turned up in Russia, where he espoused Leninism at its source.

Reforms pushed by the 4Ls did a definite service to the loggers and mill men, albeit the new wage scale seemed rather insignificant by today's standards. The per diem amount for the basic woods operations was: hook tenders - $7.00; loaders - $6.00; chokermen - $4.50; and chasers - $4.00. Of course, they lived in camp and paid a modest amount for meals at the cookhouse, thus allowing a fair amount for take home pay.

Col. Greeley went on to become Chief of the Forest Service in 1920. One of his first jobs was to prevent the national forests from being turned back to the Department of the Interior, having been in the more favorable Department of Agriculture since 1905. With the help of a friendly Secretary of Agriculture, and some powerful friends in Congress, Col. Greeley was able to carry the day.

In the St. Paul & Tacoma Lumber Company, timber operations production started to speed up after the war.

Andy Wilson was made foreman at new Camp Five on upper King Creek and Joe Chiasson was moved from Camp Two to Camp Four when it started production in 1919. Some logs were dumped into Lake Kapowsin for storage in 1920 and later that year it became evident that this would be a continuing practice. An inspection of the Four-spot shay by Hartford Steam Boiler Company found some warping in its crown sheet and some broken stay bolts. The Four-spot was the first of the heavier shays to become terminal and end up at the Camp One shop for salvage. Although it was an old friend to many, they dispensed with any rituals or the playing of Amazing Grace.

About this time, the bunkhouse talk centered on a logger named John Nordstrom from another Puget Sound area who had been working with a fellow Swede by the name of Johnson. As the story goes, they had just about completed cutting the back of a large Douglas fir up to the undercut and the last wood fibers were starting to give as they shouted "down the hill."

Nordstrom jumped to the side and heard a frantic cry from his partner. As he looked upon the scene that all fallers dread, he saw that the tree had twisted on the stump and was carrying his partner along down the slope. When Nordstrom reached Johnson he realized that his back was broken and he literally died in his arms shortly thereafter.

After bringing the body back to camp, Nordstrom helped to build a coffin of rough cedar boards and the next day brought his friend down to the waters of Puget Sound and rowed 16 miles to where he could be transferred to Seattle. After the funeral, he packed up his things and left the woods for good.

This story is typical of the human tragedy that dogged men of the woods. This kind of incident rated only a cursory reporting in the local newspaper. However, in the camps where they happened they cast a pall over the entire crew. Here was a case where the faller actually went with the tree he helped to cut — "down the hill."

Now We're Loggin'

The 1920s, often referred to as the "Roaring 20s," were good years for the St. Paul & Tacoma Lumber Company. After Mill D was constructed in Tacoma, the demand for increased logging followed, causing some dramatic changes in the logging camps. Actually, it was the agreement with Union Bag & Paper Company to dispose of much of the hemlock production that opened the door to the upland stands of timber. Major Griggs had been experimenting with storage in Lake Kapowsin and selecting areas which were predominantly Douglas fir as high priority. The pulp market acted like a relief valve and opened the way to the gung-ho mode of operation that was to follow.

A complete hi-lead crew, including choker, setters, riggers, chasers and loaders are pictured together at Camp One in 1924. Photo by C. Kinsey, University of Washington Libraries, Seattle.

Union Bag and Paper Company was a kraft mill, one that used the sulphate process for breaking down the wood fibers, and was successful in the market for what we used to call "brown paper." They, however, had no timber supply of their own and were caught up in the vicissitudes of the Great Depression, having to shut down in 1932. The plant reopened four years later under the ownership of St. Regis Paper Company, after extensive modernization.

Everyone, from the superintendent down to the lowly whistle punk, would get a lift when things went well and the usual expression was "now we're loggin'!" With the mill expansion and improved facilities at Lake Kapowsin, production reached an all time high in the mid 1920s. In 1926 the camps produced a total of more than 170 million board feet of logs. Camp One was still the headquarters for railroad operations, where the company maintained 24 miles of main line and 49 miles of spur track. It was a time of change and optimism, with a full time active engine group of six shays and two mallets.

In the early part of the decade, W. H. (Bill) Hewitt, was an active logging manager who worked out of the Tacoma office but spent a great deal of his time in the woods. Working under him was A. C. (Andy) LeDoux, who managed four camps at the time: Camp One at Ohop; Camp Two, located north of the Puyallup River near what was called Bootlegger Crossing; Camp Three, close to the south boundary of company lands in upper Ohop Creek; and Camp Four, at the extension of the Puyallup River main line above Camp Two.

Camp Four, or "Ladysville," served first as a pure logging camp and later as a base for railroad construction. Many of the camp employees walked in and out of camp on a trail that skirted around Spar Tree Hill and terminated on the Orting road near the Black Bear Tavern. The Northern Pacific Railway Company interchanged with company cars just below Camp Two, but decided to abandon this section of track in favor of a more permanent interchange just north of the Puyallup River bridge at Electron. They had at one time planned for a round house and machine shop to be located on the flat just above Camp Two.

In July of 1924, Bill Hewitt fell off a log and fractured his ribs, an accident that incapacitated him for some time. As a result, he became less active in the woods and turned over more responsibility to Andy LeDoux. When it became apparent to Bill that he was losing interest in favor of his land holdings, he resigned his position, as well as his board membership, in February of 1926. He was replaced by E. M. Rogers who assumed full charge of the woods operations. Earl Rogers never had a penchant for spending a great deal of time in the woods and increasingly headquartered in the Tacoma office, being basically a mill man. He, therefore, left the primary management of the logging operation to Andy LeDoux, the latter becoming quite adept in submitting written reports and enjoying the added responsibility.

Meanwhile, E. G. Griggs II, known as "Spike" to all his friends, had been sent years earlier to the camps by his uncle, Major Griggs, to learn the business at its source. His

Pictured is a "cold deck" of logs yarded into a pile in the Camp Three operation, and destined to be moved at a later date. Photo by C. Kinsey, University of Washington Libraries, Seattle.

first job was camp assistant clerk, actually timekeeper, at Camp One. He then went on to Camp Two as clerk, moving from there to Camp Three in August of 1920, then later that year, to purchasing agent for all the camps.

Spike was known affectionately in the woods as the "crown prince," because of the training program and family ties with the company head. He readily mixed with all the loggers and had a particular affinity with the locomotives, notably the shays. To add to his training in a management area, the Major sent him to the Nooksack operation in Whatcom County in November of 1923. When the logging of the main drainage was nearly complete, he was brought back to the Kapowsin camps once more. In a note from Major Griggs to Andy LeDoux, he asked that his nephew be located in the Tacoma office "after the first of the year when all operations and accounts are settled."

In the same note, the Major asked for Mr. Sutherland to be relocated at Camp One to be in charge of construction. Jack Sutherland had gone through several name changes in the employ of the company. In 1920, John Soderlind was a side rod and took over as foreman when Joe Chiasson left in 1922. John then became Jack Southerland. Later, when made foreman at Camp Three and on to Camp Eight when it was first built, he became Jack Sutherland. Having Anglicized his name to its fullest extent, he let it go at that.

Laying steel was a specialized job for a crew of men and the company tried to recruit from the ranks of those who had worked for the major railroad lines. The 56-pound steel could be handled by eight men who lined up on either side of the rails to be lifted. With special tong-like tools, which locked onto the upper part of the rail, the two handles came to a horizontal position when clamped, allowing sets of two men to lift and carry their section between them.

Camp Six chokers and setters, with the whistle punk at far right, stand on a bucked-to-length hemlock log. Photo by C. Kinsey, University of Washington Libraries, Seattle.

For heavier steel, or for an undermanned crew, a steel-laying donkey with two drums of equal size was used. The wire rope line was dogged to a tree or stump in line with the railroad grade and the steel pulled into place by winching. After the ties were placed at regular intervals on the finished grade the rails and plates were spiked into place. The foreman had a gauge bar which fitted over the rails at any given point to hold the steel in line for the spacing needed.

Center-dump gravel cars were pushed down the new grade where the ballast (gravel) had to be tamped down below and around the ties with square-pointed shovels. This was exhausting work and the crew usually worked in half hour shifts to keep the job going at a good pace. The steel laying crew used track jacks to lift the ties for tamping but they eschewed any comparison to the "gandy dancers" who derived their name from the use of jacks, preferring to remain a cut above the maintenance gang.

North Brooks, after his stint as logging contract logger at Camp Six, retired to become a maintenance man and lord major at the gravel source, always referred to as the "pit." He had his cabin, garage and smoke house, where he held sway and became somewhat of a martinet. When he passed away in 1946, the funeral parlor in Orting was filled to capacity. There was a lone, mystery woman in black who broke out in sobs during the ceremony, then left before any explanation could be given. We always wondered — North was never any Rudolph Valentino.

In the course of logging, some accidents happened in spite of safety precautions, particularly when the odds were increased by running a full blower operation as was the case in the 1920s. It was a Monday morning in June, 1924, when Tom Thompson and his partner were in the process of finishing the back cut on a large cedar tree that had a noticeable hollow center. Before they could "call" the tree, a section on Thompson's side suddenly separated from the trunk and kicked out in a sideward fashion. The blow ruptured all his internal organs and he expired within minutes.

This phenomenon was not strictly a thing called by loggers "barber chairing" because the split was very localized, probably caused by an internal strain from the tree having a definite lean. The chances of this happening and the probability of Thompson being in the precise spot at the wrong time were quite remote. In any event, his friends had to bury him.

E. W. (Ernie) Allison started his career with the company at Camp Four in 1916 as a donkey puncher. Later, as a side rod, he was helping out loading logs and had one roll down on him, partially crushing his leg. After recovering, he was able to walk quite handily, albeit with a definite limp that handicapped him for much of the woods work. He was made foreman at Camp One in 1920 and remained there until he was made superintendent on December 1 of 1931.

Railroads, camps, wire rope, donkey punchers, gandy dancers ... the list of ingredients that made up what we

Engineer Dave Voss (far left) stands on the company's first Willamette Skider. Photo by C. Kinsey, University of Washington Libraries, Seattle.

know of the logging industry thrived in the 1920s. It was the big yarders, however, that changed things most dramatically. By means of the high lead, we could reach out farther, have fewer hangups and leave the ground relatively undamaged. Back in August of 1909 The Timberman carried an article lauding the merits of the Lidgerwood overhead skidder. Its multiple drum system and carriage, with a slack puller to bring down the chokers at any point, became the most innovative and progressive machine of its time.

From this point on, the machinery and rigging advances led to a speed-up and power gain, which together with increased efficiency, culminated in the mid 1920s. We went from spar trees topped at 60 to 70 feet to those up to 160 feet. We went from steel spars that could be moved by railroad car (limit of 80 feet in height) to raised trees where guy lines were shackled while on the ground. We went from the Lidgerwood type of yarding to the skyline type where a tight line held by tree jacks went from the head spar to a tail tree out a good 1500 feet. This system could reach much farther to the side than other methods, but even better, it almost eliminated hangups.

It was Andy LeDoux who was the "push" for the enlarged forest operations during these "now we're loggin'" days where up to five camps were active at a given time. He was well known as a womanizer, but it was a petty indiscretion that ultimately brought him down. A private sale of wire rope was discovered and his dismissal was announced in November of 1931.

All of this increased activity quite suddenly changed when the stock market crashed in 1929, followed by the Great Depression in the early 1930s. These were the days I remember most vividly as the glamour of the woods operations was tempered by immediate family needs. It was a time of expectations and doubts about personal fulfillment.

Delegates to the Pacific Logging Congress are shown in 1922. They are (left to right) John Nerbonne, E.M. Rogers, Nels Soderlind, E.G. Griggs, Andy LeDoux, Bill Hewitt, Spike Griggs (in the foreground) and N.G. Jacobson (above on platform at far right). Photo courtesy of the Washington State Historical Society.

The Lure Of The Logging Camp

The year was 1927 and it was a good year for the country, and for me as well. We moved to a new house that provided me with a secluded bedroom and most of the second story to develop as my own. In one of my visits to the St. Paul & Tacoma Lumber Company main office, I met the president, Major Griggs, and had a chance to hold my father's pearl handled security revolver, which was kept near the cash drawer. But more important — Lindbergh landed in France and became an outstanding American ambassador of good will. The first radio telephone call was made between London and New York, and in downtown Tacoma, the first talking picture was showing at the

Blue Mouse Theatre; all pretty heady stuff for a young fellow to digest.

1927 was also the year that my father decided that a family visit to the logging camps was in order. We arrived at Camp One early in the morning and were met by Porter Brown, the steward for all the camps. What an adventure was in store for us! He was a big man and seemed to dominate the little speeder that was our transportation for the day. We sat side saddle and when crossing a trestle there was an altogether nothingness between the foot board and the bottom of the gully.

It seemed like hours before we arrived at Camp Six, a car or wheel camp on the south side of Voight Creek. We were in plenty of time for lunch and what a great experience it was for my sister and me to actually sit with the camp crew. We checked out the office car, a typical bunkhouse, the kitchen area and cold locker, all of the things that represented story book stuff for urban youngsters. This was a fairly new location for the camp but the logging was several miles away and not available to us. We did, however, get to see a trainload of logs come through the camp and on down the main line.

My most vivid memory of Camp Six was a visit to the storehouse where they kept the staples such as flour, sugar, beans, etc. It was Hugh Brown, Porter's son, who took me aside and promised a real sight. We had to sneak up on the storehouse car platform like of couple of London footpads. With a last touch of his finger to the lips, Hugh threw open the door and — the place was alive with pack rats! They scattered in all directions and disappeared through the many holes that had been gnawed in the lower walls. The fact that they sported bushy tails like squirrel's didn't alleviate the shock treatment. It was only Hugh's guffaw that brought me back to normalcy. So much for Camp Six.

Back down the Voight Creek main line we took a switchback and started to climb the hillside. I can remember well crossing three high trestles that still invoked a white knuckle response in spite of getting used to this mode of travel. At the top of the hill we coasted into the compound of Camp Eight, a newly constructed array of bunkhouses and service buildings with connecting elevated walkways. They were freshly painted the traditional St. Paul gray, all crowded inside three railroad spurs that formed a concave "Y." Altogether a modern prototype of the "new look" in logging camps.

Two memorable incidents stand out in this visit to Camp Eight. First, the pastry cook had just taken out of the oven a large pan of cinnamon rolls, freshly basted with frosting. These, together with some mugs of ice-cold milk, became the ultimate piece de resistance for the starry-eyed visitors. Competing with this treat was the sight of a construction crew making up the sled base for an oversized donkey, one of the new heavy-duty skidders. Two large diameter Douglas fir logs were barked and then fashioned by hand with tapered snipings at each end. With spuds and broad axes these men looked like flensers dismantling a whale as the chips were flying from both ends and from the notches for the cross members.

Later, our speeder trip brought us back down to cross the Puyallup River, past Lake Kapowsin and up the Ohop Creek Valley to Camp One once again. We stopped for a brief while to check a few things and got the block to proceed up the main line to Camp Three.

Actually, this was the third so-numbered camp. The first was north of the Puyallup River in the King Creek area and the second was near the old homestead of Joseph

McMinn at the south fork of Ohop Creek. This newer camp was located in a strategic saddle where the drainage went both east and west, commanding a beautiful view of the upper Puyallup River Valley and Mt. Rainier.

It was late in the afternoon when we arrived. After visiting the cookhouse, office and a couple of bunkhouses, we were met by the foreman, Nels Soderlind. He immediately caught my fancy because of his friendly and somewhat gentle nature, quite at variance to the expected stereotype of a "bull of the woods." It eventually turned out to be a lasting and valuable friendship, as I later worked with him as engineer and forester.

Back in Camp One, it was close to dinner time so we joined the entire logging crew in the cookhouse. The gut hammer beating on the iron triangle at the entrance called us all in. However, most of the loggers were already on the

Cooks, flunkies and dishwashers at Camp Three in 1926. Photo by C. Kinsey, University of Washington Libraries, Seattle.

porch and rushed in, almost in a stampede. After the clanking of heavy dinnerware they settled down to what can only be described as "wolfing it." The remarkable thing was an almost complete lack of conversation and the place was nearly empty before we could start our dessert. I was later to become part of this and to better understand their strange behavior.

It was then back to our venerable Maxwell and down the hill to the Orting highway and home. Just after crossing the Puyallup River, we looked back in the blackness of night and saw a blaze of light high on top of the hill. This turned out to be what was called "electric camp," the terminal of the Puget Sound Power & Light Company flume line and head of the penstock that developed the pressure for the power plant below.

The next visit to the woods operations was in 1929 and under quite different circumstances. My father had been diagnosed with a wasting disease and the doctor felt he had improved chances of recovery by living in camp where clean air, good food and a more vigorous lifestyle would serve him well. He arranged for a leave of absence for me from junior high school and we shared a bunkhouse in Camp One and lived the life of special guests.

Major Griggs had previously arranged to have the Camp One area platted into Elkhorn additions One, Two and Three. Permanent residents then had fee simple deeds to their chosen property. The company built a one room schoolhouse to accommodate the family progeny, and it was to this dedication to the learning process that I spent the balance of the school semester. As in the traditional country schoolhouse, grade levels were placed in rows and took turns for recitation. It is a tribute to these hardy teachers that they were able to educate youngsters without counselors, nurses, librarians, custodians and other necessities of today, not to mention visual aids and stress therapy, etc.

Unfortunately, the doctor's prescription for my father's recovery failed to bring about any improvement. His health continued to fail and we lost him in March of 1930. He often told me that his wish was for me to attend Stanford University and pursue a course in electrical engineering, a sure bet for the future as he saw it. The day I walked through the main entrance to the University of Washington, I actually did pause and reflect about my inner feelings. In the end, I turned to the right and followed what seemed to me a proper heritage — to Anderson Hall and the College of Forestry for my undergraduate registry.

The one-room schoolhouse at Camp One where the author attended sixth grade. Photo courtesy of University of Washington Libraries, Seattle.

The Old Order Changeth

By the end of the century's second decade the Great Depression was beginning to take its toll on the timber and lumber industries — St. Paul & Tacoma Lumber Company fell into line by necessity. Woods crews were streamlined and production curtailed. Cutbacks in milling and office personnel kept the company afloat for several years but it found itself gradually losing ground.

At this same time the Hewitt Land Company, now tied into the lumber company through inter-locking directorships, found that land ownership was "overtaxing." It had to rely on the Tacoma branch of the Bank of California to bail it out for 1930 taxes. This later spread to the lumber company, where a decision was made to place a business manager in the office to act as comptroller. The bank's representative, Mr. Whitaker, known by his minions as "Whit," somewhat resembled Alfred Hitchcock and was the butt of snide remarks behind his back.

Chauncey L. Griggs, nephew of Major Griggs, had been placed by him to work with Henry Dennis at Camp Three to learn the timber business. Henry was acting as assistant superintendent under Andy LeDoux at the time, but the dwindling demand for lumber forced him to be transferred to engineering. Orville Shaw, chief engineer, was bumped and O. E. (Bud) Scharf was transferred from Camp Eight to Camp Seven at Deming, Washington.

Having been foreman at Camp One since 1920, Ernie Allison was the obvious choice for superintendent of woods operations when Andy LeDoux was fired in December of 1931. Ernie was to serve for many years in this capacity until retirement age caught up with him in 1942. As a superintendent he proved to be the best in the company's history, both as a tactician and as a supervisor of men.

Ernie had one feature that fell short of being a redeeming one — he had a fixation on the logistics of logging, which many interpreted as mind wandering. For instance, he sometimes forgot to change the switch back after going through it on his speeder and caused problems with those that followed. The only time it really inconvenienced him was when he neglected to reset the derail coming into the Puyallup River interchange and had a rough ride on the gravel for over a hundred feet.

On several occasions I rode down from Camp Five to Camp One with him in the company of the elder flunkey who would scream when the wheels shrieked against the rails while crossing trestles. Ernie did not bother to change speed; he just sat back with his arms folded while managing a fleeting smile. The flunkey did not know what I did, that a trestle with non-shifting steel and heavy guard rails was safer than heavy curves on solid ground.

One winter day, I met Ernie in Orting and mentioned that he had a bad crease on the right side of his new Chrysler Imperial. He just shrugged his shoulders and said, "Yeh, that rock that sticks out on the way down from Camp One. I'll match it on the other side going back." That was the same winter when he suddenly tried to brake on sheer ice, also in Orting, where his car turned over on its side and slid for a long distance before coming to a stop. Ernie was evidently logging again and neglected to check his speed.

Depression years seemed to be an inauspicious time for Dempsey Lumber Company to start operations on its lands near Camp One, but they went ahead because of the big investment in a new Tacoma mill. Jim Dempsey made a deal with St. Paul & Tacoma Lumber Company to bring in ballast for track laying on company gravel cars at the rate of 10 cents per mile. Dempsey had two Heisler locomotives and was to deliver logs to Camp One as well as pick up gravel cars at that point. St. Paul & Tacoma Lumber Company agreed to use their mallets to deliver log cars to the Northern Pacific interchange near Lake Kapowsin at the rate of $7.00 per car. The first logs made it to the Dempsey mill in the summer of 1931.

In St. Paul & Tacoma Lumber Company's main office changes were being made of great importance. Major Griggs had always been keen on the management of forest lands to provide continuous production. The Reforestation Act of 1931 allowed logged-off lands to remain at an assessed rate of $1.00 per acre until harvested again, at which time the land owner was required to pay a 12 1/2%

yield tax, based on value removed. E. T. Allen was retained
in 1927 to make a study and recommend a long term plan
for the stewardship of company forest lands. Allen's
associate, Norman G. Jacobson, was called to assist, staying
on after the primary study in an advisory capacity.

Several years later Major Griggs created a land
department and hired "Jake" on a permanent basis.
Jacobson was a 1910 graduate from the University of
Minnesota and found his place with the newly created
United States Forest Service. He at one time was the admin-
istrator of the service lands in eastern Oregon. After leaving

*Norman Jacobson (right) is shown talking with camp bull
bucker. From the author's collection.*

Uncle Sam in favor of private forestry he sustained a serious accident that left him partially crippled. Because he refused the necessary surgery to repair the hip injury, his later years left him with an impaired ability to get around in a normal fashion.

Nineteen thirty three was a year which changed the complexion of the company's operations, particularly at the administration level. In August of that year, Major Griggs lost control of his car and suffered serious injuries. Worse still, his passenger, Herbert Griggs, died several days later as a result of the accident. Chauncey L. Griggs, who had spent some time in the woods and was serving as assistant secretary, was named to succeed his father, H. S. Griggs.

Major Griggs never really recovered robust health after the accident and felt that it was time to turn the reins over to someone who could carry on in the manner he envisioned. Certainly E. G. (Spike) Griggs had the most training in the woods operations, and since the Major had no children, it seemed appropriate to defer to his namesake. Spike moved into the front office at 1220 St. Paul Avenue in the fall of 1933.

To complete the new look at the management level, G. Corydon Wagner, son of Dr. George Wagner and grandson of Col. Chauncey Griggs, was named vice president. Cordy, as he was better known, had a penchant for the business end, so he took over his part of the duties. Since Spike Griggs had never shown much interest in milling and sales, Cordy also was designated to administer these divisions.

Problems developed in the woods operations during 1933. The Voight Creek main line was being pushed up the south side of the valley. However, too much hemlock was being projected so the activity was substantially curtailed. The estimation of 150 million board feet as projected in

March had to be cut back to less than half that amount by September. In December of 1933 the Puyallup River main line was flooded and partially washed out. The loss of six weeks' logging time prompted Ernie Allison to recommend abandoning it altogether. Spike Griggs agreed and asked Henry Dennis to look into an alternate route to tap the upper Puyallup valley.

Meanwhile, the LeDoux family had continuing problems. After the forced termination of Andy, there was some pressure to reconsider Joe LeDoux for promotion. Bunkhouse jokes were rampant about his basic intelligence. It was said that Joe could look through a keyhole without closing one eye (the equivalent of being too narrow between the eyes). In June of 1934, Donald LeDoux, who had been a timekeeper at Camp Eight, took a risk in trying to cross the track between log cars while off the job. At that moment, the loci humped the string and Donald was caught between the drawheads. The last of the LeDoux logging personnel ended up as watchman at Camp Five in the early 1940s.

When I came to work for St. Paul & Tacoma Lumber Company in 1939 the office talk concerned Chauncey Griggs and his a.w.o.l. trip to Tahiti. Nobody was advised of his whereabouts until a telegram arrived notifying the company of his self-imposed vacation. When he arrived back in the office he described life in Polynesia, accompanied by a drumming on his desk and a faraway look in his eyes. Cordy was not amused and this incident probably precipitated the rift between them that was to play such an important part in years to come.

My first job for the company was to evaluate many scattered portions of logged-off lands that were becoming tax delinquent. We ended up by redeeming those parcels that had some resale value and letting the county take over

Camp Five before the disastrous burn of 1940. Pictured from left to right are Ed Stryken, Henry Dennis, Superintendent Ernie Allison and George Zoffel. Photo courtesy of University of Washington Libraries, Seattle.

a few areas that had no potential value as growing sites. The company had a firm policy for handling resales — $10.00 per acre with as little as $10.00 down and interest on the unpaid balance at 6%.

Before the Major left the company's presidency he directed Jacobson to register some 70,000 acres of prime forest-growing land under the Reforestation Act of 1931. By 1939, it became the policy to call a halt to this process because the value for second growth was starting to rise quite dramatically, while assessed valuations were being kept at a reasonable level. Years later I was destined to administer the first second-growth thinning program that required paying the 12 1/2% yield tax.

With Camp Three located on a strategic saddle looking into the upper Puyallup River basin, it was considered as a possible continuing base camp for most of the company timber to the east. Henry Dennis ran a preliminary line into this large area and observed that less than three miles of adverse grade could bring all the logs to the saddle junction known as "30" (from the section number). With Ernie Allison's blessing, the new main line was built down into the Puyallup basin, which opened up the *Mowich River basin as well. (* Mowich is the Chinook word for deer.)

And so it was that Camp Five was built just a few hundred feet south of the upper Puyallup River. It opened in February of 1935 and had three sides going by mid summer. At first, this main line was called Branch Two, with Branch One going north from "30" and Branch Three going east and south to tap the upper basins of the Mashel River and

Pictured is the author's home at Camp Five. It was typical of the wood bungalows built in the 1950s. From the author's collection.

the Busywild drainage at the extreme southern edge of company property. This latter main line was projected to access St. Paul & Tacoma Lumber Company's last logging camp.

Many large logs had been brought in to the Tacoma mill from the early camps, particularly in the 1920s. I remember measuring a stump close to Camp One that was well over 9 feet in diameter. The record, however, was to come out of Camp Five in October of 1935. This big Douglas fir yielded 45,490 board feet as it was cut into four sections. The stump measurement at six feet above ground was 10 feet, 6 inches.

Fire Is A Bad Actor

Under a microscope the composition of wood is made clear; it is constructed of fibers, specialized cells, vessels, xylem and phloem areas, mixed with a complex variety of chemical substances such as resins and sugars. Altogether, wood is a marvel of nature with many attributes that have served mankind through the ages. Unfortunately, it is readily destructible by fire. The living, coniferous tree has a crown that is quite combustible and can lead to vulnerability when heated to a critical stage.

In all recorded history of the Northwest, the fire season of 1902 was the most devastating. It represented the greatest loss of marketable timber in our time. The Yacolt burn was so extensive that no combination of logging and milling alliances could have salvaged enough timber to make a significant dent in the vast acreage lost. It was also a devastating year in other parts of Washington State as a pall rivaling that of Krakatoa hung over all the West. Olympia suspended business, electric lights and streetcars ceased to operate, all because of low water at the power dam. Many thought that Mt. Rainier had once again erupted.

The St. Paul & Tacoma Lumber Company woods operations were lucky to survive the severe fire danger with only minor losses. However, the town of Enumclaw and its environs were not so fortunate. The local newspaper carried the story, "Every team in town is pressed into service. Not a man here is not exhausted by 16 hours on the fire lines to save this town."

From the Seattle Post Intelligencer of September 15, 1902: "News has just reached here that the forest fires on Lewis River have wrought sad havoc. D. L. Wallace and wife and two children were burned to death. They were camping in the woods and were caught by fire. A twelve year-old boy of Mr. Henley is dead also. Mr. Newhouse and Mrs. Graves are dead. Fifteen others were found without clothing except gunny sacks."

In the September 19, 1902 issue of the Orting Oracle it was noted that Montesano, Washington was cut off from its neighbors as "heavy forest fires have been ranging throughout this county all day and have occasioned many thousands of dollars loss with reports of loss of life, which up to this hour cannot be confirmed although the sources from which the information was derived, it is feared the reports are true."

Headlines of "Immense Loss of Property is Certain," "Day Made as Night" and "Darkness Covers Entire Western

Portion of Two States" appeared in the local papers. Many logging camps were burned and reports came in from all over the Northwest of loss of life. Boats on the Columbia River had to use searchlights to navigate. A separate fire in King County burned out communication lines between Seattle and Everett and a pall of smoke ranged all the way up to the Canadian border. Lessons learned from these extensive fires were used to modify the fire code in woods operations, also changing many of the laissez-faire attitudes that prevailed in some quarters.

Burning slash after logging had been the custom ever since the early days of timber harvesting. This so-called controlled burning lowered the fire hazard for a while but destroyed the understory that survived the yarding operation. Later, it became almost a must because properly-burned slash carried with it a certificate from the State relieving the land owner's liability for accidental fire damage at a later date.

The overriding problem that has always existed is that, by definition, a successful slash burn is one that almost gets away. One of them that did indeed get away occurred on May 29, 1922. This was the attempt to burn the accumu-lated slash between Camp One and Camp Three. As is often the case, the timing seemed to be right. The late bad weather brought hail and some wet snow on May 23, which appeared to be a deterrent for fire spreading.

All went well and the burn seemed to be nearly complete. The turn of events was best described by bull bucker Nels Soderlind, who had worked his crew through the night and returned to his bunkhouse about 5:30 A.M. "They woke me up at 11:00 A.M. and the fire was then down within 100 feet of my shack. The wind was blowing then from the southeast at a terrific gale."

Crews from all the camps fought the fire all through the month of June as it would break out from time to time and cross the fire line. After many heartbreaking incidents, when it appeared to be finally out, the final solution came on July 15 when the last smoke was extinguished. It was an expensive operational experience. The cost of fighting the burnout rose into five figures, not to mention the consumption of ten million board feet of logs. The 880 acres of green timber burned was largely salvaged. This was the last time that slash was burned in the springtime. Fall burning had the advantage of moisture closing in when things went awry.

Camps themselves are vulnerable to fire, as we were to discover. Back in 1933, Ernie Allison, superintendent, recommended two new camps to be constructed: one near the Puyallup River and one on the west slope of Mt. Rainier near the Rushingwater River. The former was built and became Camp Five, the latter never materialized.

It all happened on July 1, 1940 when Camp Five was shut down and only five men remained in camp on a maintenance basis. It was Emil Barkost, who discovered the fire and had left the power plant a scant five minutes earlier. The cause of the fire was listed as a short circuit in the auxiliary power unit but many fingers pointed to Emil for pulling some kind of bonehead stunt to trigger the blaze. I have always thought that an accidental fire was much more convenient from a liability standpoint than the possible alternative.

In any event, the short crew tried to hook up a hose, rather tardily, to water down the locomotive house, but the cookhouse roof caved in soon after and broke the water line. Wipe out one major logging camp! Everything burned to the ground except the oil house and five residences at the lower end, which were somewhat removed from the main camp.

As a result of the fire, portions of burned Northern Pacific Railway Company lands were purchased by the company as compensation for loss. Lack of vigilance could prove to be expensive.

When it came time to burn slash the entire camp turned out, from side rods to whistle punks. They, unfortunately, did not have much rapport with a drip torch and usually went about setting spot fires with a grumbling acquiescence. As a result, the job of burning out small sections up to the fire line and then progressing down the hill required patience and care. Evidently some of this was missing in the Voight Creek Valley slash burn on September 29, 1942.

Reports started coming in late in the afternoon that all was not well when the fire started growing too fast and creating its own wind. By early evening, the crew started a panic exodus, particularly whose who had their cars parked up on the old spur at the head of the access trail. Just before midnight, the Three-spot arrived and was able to hook on and remove the office car and one other. Speeders picked up all those who had not left previously and brought them on down to Electron. As sometimes is the case, by freak happenstance, the fire wiped out all the buildings that had to be left except one at each end of the camp.

The fire of 1942 was the most extensive in company history — a little over 10,000 acres, mostly logged-off land. It was the impetus for an ambitious planting program in which more than eight million trees were hand-planted, with an average survival rate of 72%. The old timers would have marvelled at the genetic improvement plans that followed, using elite trees as scions for root-stock grafting.

Demon fire was still not through with pyrotechniques as a slash burn jumped the prepared fire lines on October

27, 1944, burning a watchman's house and flat car, as well as quite a bit of logging equipment. The biggest loss from this fire was 1,465,000 board feet of logs in a cold deck, together with the rigging and a yarder. The 141 acres of timber burned was largely salvaged.

Men Of The Camps

Logging camps never developed men of the stripe to compare with Paul Bunyan and Jigger Jones, but in their time, they were well represented with compelling personalities and individualistic traits. The men often referred to themselves as "brush apes." However, when writers wished to give them a little more flourish, they often used the name "timber beasts." In any event, the loggers and their fellow workers have always been characterized as a special breed, and rightfully so.

Dinner time at the cookhouse was an unvarying study in anticipation. The anteroom and the front porch were always crowded with men straining to get an advantageous position. When the second cook came out to beat on the triangle with the gut hammer the double doors crashed open with bodies rushing to their personal seats. There was very little conversation at the tables, only the sound of silverware and dinnerware with occasional asking of things to be passed. This was usually interpreted as the "dog in the manger" syndrome, which appeared indigenous to the logging camps.

Thanksgiving and Christmas time called for special procedures. My first time for these occasions made me wonder why everyone was carrying a paper bag into the cookhouse. The mystery was solved when I saw everyone chucking in candy, nuts, special cookies, fruit, etc. before even turning over their plates. Later I discovered much of this booty languishing on the bunkhouse window sills. It must have seemed like a good idea at the time.

In point of fact, selfishness was not an established trait

Meal time at Camp Five, circa 1946. The cook-house could feed up to 300 men. Courtesy of the Tacoma Public Library.

Camp crews in the second growth forest near old Camp Six pose for posterity in 1932. The man to the far left with his dog is Nels Soderlind. Photo by C. Kinsey, University of Washington Libraries, Seattle.

with the men of the camps as was demonstrated on many occasions. Very likely a psychology student would probably say that the behavior manifested an innate fear of deprivation, which surfaced after the Great Depression. Loggers were always good contributors to charities and they emptied their wallets for the families of those who became victims of fatal accidents.

Typical of the Swede logger was my special woods personality Nels Soderlind. One incident stands out among many when I think back upon my acquaintance with Nels. Soon after we occupied the last Camp Two the men were having problems with dysentery and the brownish-tinged water supply was suspect. A committee from the crew came to me, knowing my connection with the company executives, to ask for a scientific check to me made. I brought in a sample jar to Spike Griggs and asked him to authorize a laboratory analysis.

A week or so later, when Nels and I were talking over the day's happenings, the camp clerk brought in his mail. As he put on his granny glasses and opened up an important-looking envelope, it proved to be the lab report in question. With some degree of internal control, I heard him stumble over some Latin names, all coliform bacteria. He made it through Proteus in good fashion, but was all over the field when it came to Aerobacter aerogenes and Pseudomonas fluorescens, obviously culprits in the camp problem. Nels interpreted it quite another way. He looked at me over his granny glasses and said, "Yeezus Christ Roy, dat' gud vater!"

It was a result of the previous Camp Two going up in smoke that I came to know Mike Lulich. On our long ride from temporary camp quarters at the old C.C.C. camp at Electron to the woods operations, I usually chose the trailer, known as the "cooler" because it lacked any heat. Dan "Black Mike" Lulich was the rail maintenance foreman and was noted for his strength and endurance with a track maul. During the winter of 1942-'43, we had some icy days and Mike often said, "Hey keed, come over and sit here," as he patted the seat next to him in a sort of paternalistic gesture. He was a man of few words but we did share a big rapport in that small, close-up world.

Men of the track crew used to jack up the rails temporarily while tamping in ballast, hence were given the name of "gandy dancers" as they jumped up and down on the jack handle. Black Mike always had one eye on the track when travelling by speeder, looking for gaps, loose "Dutchmen" or sags that needed ballasting to lift back into place.

A "Dutchman" could be a short section of rail to fill in a separation of track but quite often was piece of switch rail that tapered to a point. The latter was put in place with the tapered portion on the outside and overlapping the rail already in place. These tapered sections looked positively unnerving when you were traveling at a good speed. However, they accomplished their purpose and saved major repairs.

It was Mike's habit of riding in front on the track speeder that led to his demise one foggy day in 1944. Our big turret speeder was hauling a large trailer load of diesel barrels going up to Camp Two on this particular day. At the siding below camp, Rex Rushforth, the driver, had dogged or jill-poked the trailer he had been pushing to run around it — it was unlawful to "bald face" into the camp area. By the time he arrived back to hook on, he found that the trailer had somehow cut loose, jumped the frog (switch unit) and was somewhere loose on the main line.

Gandy dancers were members of a track gang posed here with their tools piled on a small flat car at Camp Two. Note the "Mulligan Cans" (lunch boxes) in the foreground. From the author's collection.

Pictured is a turret speeder connected to a trailer which is loading the woods crew for return to Camp One. Photo by C. Kinsey, University of Washington Libraries, Seattle.

In a sequence of unlikely events, which would have normally derailed the trailer, its weight and momentum caused it to career down the track for a good one and a half miles and crash into Mike's track speeder as it was making its way back to camp. Because of the fog, there was little or no warning and Black Mike was killed instantly. Others were hurt in the crash, but only the driver, Art Barber, had serious injuries, being hospitalized for several weeks with broken bones. For years, the flattened diesel barrels and pieces of orange plywood from the trailer body were seen along the main line as a grim reminder. I lost an out-of-the-ordinary friend on that day.

In the early 1940s, a popular professional wrestler came into the national limelight. These were the beginning times for the more colorful wrestlers who were to catch the public's fancy. Such an individual was "The Angel," a stocky fireplug of a man whose shaven head and coarse features were set upon broad shoulders with only the benefit of a rudimentary neck — altogether the stereotype of a thug.

Strikingly similar to The Angel was Vito Tosco, a track worker or gandy dancer working out of Camp Five. He was a prodigious eater and had a particular affinity for pork chops. On the way out of the cookhouse one evening, an acquaintance of his called after him, "Hey Vito, I counted — you ate fourteen pork chops!" Vito wheeled around, his face flushed, and shouted back, "Atsa bigga lie, I only eata thirteen!"

As a tree topper and rigger, Phil Grabinski was one of the last of the all-time loggers. He held the climbing record for many years with an ascent of 150 feet on a spar tree, returning to the ground in one minute and twenty seconds. Still the record, as far as I know, is the raising of a 172 foot spar tree near Camp One and the snubbing of four top guys in eight minutes flat. Grabinski was the climber and Bill McAbee the side rod.

Phil Grabinski turned up again on a side near the Rushingwater circa 1944. He had set up a skyline system where a man rode the carriage and had direct control of the fall block and chokers. Since nobody wanted to try it out, he became his own guinea pig. The Grabinski system worked, but the risk did not outweigh the advantage of precision and selectivity. It went the way of many other good ideas that did not sell.

Sometimes it seemed that a tree topper and rigger led a charmed life. Such a phenomenon was Haywire Tom Watson who worked out of a logging camp on the Olympic Peninsula. In the words of one of his fellow workman who recalled the incident, "I was working with him in the woods one day, and I saw him fall 120 feet, while going up a fir.

Clinging to a swaying Douglas fir 120 feet above the ground, a tree topper is shown just after finishing a cut. Photo courtesy of University of Washington Libraries, Seattle.

He hit the mud first. The deep, soft mud cushioned his fall and when they drove him off, he was still smiling and waving his arms, as if in victory over death. The doc found nothing wrong with him, so he put his clothes back on and came to work."

Engineer and rigging crew pose in front of tree, clinging to which is a man using a cable core climbing rope, with long spurs attached to his boots. Photo courtesy of University of Washington Libraries, Seattle.

Another good bunkhouse story centered around the days when loggers were sometimes Shanghaied onto sailing ships that needed deck hands. One enterprising entrepreneur put aboard a cigar store Indian wrapped in a tarpaulin thought to be stiff from booze. The captain was assured that there was nothing like good sea air to sober up a logger.

When I first met Steve Thomas, he was a state game warden, but he had spent much time before working in the camps and was certainly woods-wise. He had a particular knack for catching poachers and had a top rating as a beaver trapper. In 1943 we had a flooding problem on Fox Creek where a forty acre area was under water and the trees were all dying. Steve managed to clear all but a pair of beavers (the last of a colony always leave before their own demise) and saved the day for our budding forest.

Our pet deer, Anges, and raccoon, Cosmo, were a result of Steve finding a home for orphaned animals that

Here is a steel-laying crew working out of Camp One in 1924. Photo by C. Kinsey, University of Washington Libraries, Seattle.

could be kept in a somewhat normal habitat. Although usually all business, he sometimes did some pretty serious off-duty tippling. On one notable occasion, he thought it was a good idea to have some fun with a bobcat that he had caught in a trap.

Saturday night at the Electron Tavern was always a big one when the loggers packed the place for drink and conversation. On this particular night, Steve brought in a gunny sack and with a heave at the end of the bar, emptied the sack of its contents. When the bobcat came sliding down the bar digging its claws into the polished surface and snarling all the way, all hell broke loose and no fire drill could have emptied the place with such dispatch.

Regal language is something one would never attribute to hardy, but often tongue-tied woodsmen. Nevertheless, in a report from Camp One to C. L. Pierce, Tacoma office manager, dated November 11, 1920, this courtly language was used: "Now I take my pen in hand to answer some of your most pressing inquiries, covered by your most esteemed favor of the 15th of September..." signed: D.F. Moore, clerk.

Part of the passing parade was the indomitable North Brooks, part logger, timber cruiser, maintenance man and watchman. He prefaced all of his more adamant remarks with "By the Jesus Christ!" Then there was "Haywire Johnson," later called "Pipeline Johnson" who was always seen with his Stillson Wrench, but his most distinguishing feature was a permanent ring of snoose stain around his mouth, while his head bobbed in an apparently uncontrollable fashion. "Black Douglas" was certainly the most memorable of the engineers as he defied the fire of 1918 and lost his life in the Puyallup River Canyon near the Puget Sound Power & Light Company flume line.

Old Ed Shiek, who fired up a skidder in the early morning and doubled as a watchman, was a memorable character. In our infrequent visits to his shack for a mid-day warming, we invariably had to turn down his invitation for supplementary lunch — he never heard about what is next to godliness, as the only part of him that wasn't black, were his hands after peeling potatoes.

They are all gone now. Even the proverbial echoes no longer resonate as the big timber is replaced by a more vibrant second growth. The camps are grown over with only a hint of their former presence in broken dishes, twisted pipe sections, rotted railroad ties and the like. Just a handful of old timers remain to remember the flavor of it all.

Men of the woods are shown next to a loaded flatcar in 1926. Standing is the foreman, Nels Soderlind; sitting on the log is Fred Woodery, head loader. From the author's collection.

A Matter Of Introspection

To say that loggers only dealt with the here and now is over-simplification and one must always reckon with the "I know somebody who ... group." Nevertheless, they were true realists and were busy in a hazardous occupation where self-preservation had a high priority. It is understandable that they became somewhat inured to accidents and even fatalities because of the frequency of these incidents.

The use of seven blasts of a yarder's whistle always had been a sound to send chills up one's spine. It was notice of a serious accident, sometimes fatal, often resulting in the demise of more than one person. In the old days, it was customary to bring the body(ies) to the landing and continue working the full day. It was not considered so much of a callous gesture, as it was a rationalization of the futility in becoming emotionally involved.

There can be no stereotype of a logger if we think of him as a composite of all the operations attendant to the harvesting of trees. Closest to nature, however, would be the cruisers, engineers and fallers. They experienced the pristine state of nature and all the impinging factors that formed the old growth forest. By the time the riggers and yarding crew arrived on the scene there was a static sameness that dictated feelings to go with a job to be done. Nevertheless, it was apparent that a common thread ran through whatever metaphysical feelings were present in those who worked in this unique industry.

Although not inscrutable in the sense of a cunning person, there was a measure of withdrawal in nearly all of those who worked in the woods. From the bushelers who sat with folded hands on their bunks and stared at the floor, to the wood's foreman of few words, theirs was a world of internalizing. It was only after a long exposure to loggers' thoughts that I was able to generalize about the spiritual nature of woodsman.

Unlike the saying there are "no atheists in a foxhole," probably few true-believers in religious orthodoxy were to be found in the logging genre. This, perhaps, could be attributed to loggers being close to nature, the idea of survival of the fittest, together with the concept that random happenings were seen to be a matter of course. I found only a handful who believed that their lives were programmed. What may appear on the outside as stoicism, was probably an inward air of confidence.

The concept of life after death was certainly a conundrum that mystified those men of the timber, whose very existence was dependent upon pragmatism for survival.

It has been my impression that the average logger had his own brand of agnostic belief, one in which he found it difficult to embrace a personal God, or to find himself important enough for any form of continuity after death where awareness was a factor. He did, nevertheless, because of his unique surroundings, have a concept of natural rhythms and the mysteries of instinct, which in the animal world defied explanation.

The bunkhouse Bible was not a complete rarity, but was used primarily for those who wished to keep in touch with organized religions, usually family-oriented. There were probably just as many avowed atheists as agnostics; at least the former tended to be more outspoken. My closest confident, while working in the logging operations, was quite adamant about his beliefs. Henry Beane, together with a handful of casual acquaintances, certainly embraced the notion of the black curtain and oblivion as man's inheritance. He seemed quite content with this thought and appeared to shrug off any feelings of dread and intimidation.

Perhaps everyone has had a quasi-religious experience, somewhat akin to an out-of-the-body sensation. For me the most vivid occurred during my first winter at new Camp Two. It was an early February morning when we heard that the turret speeder had broken down and we were to be taken to the logging sides in the Mowich area by flat car and locomotive.

It was still dark and a light scuff of snow had fallen during the night, which had given way to absolute stillness. We climbed onto the flats by brushing off the snow and placing sections of corrugated cartons to sit on, feet hanging over the side with insulation on the back side making it quite comfortable.

It appeared that the logging crew could feel a strangeness because those few who were talking were doing so in whispers. Looking down into camp from our perch, there was a scene of mysterious serenity as the snow sparkled on top of every bunkhouse from the pole lights; the flattened layer of smoke from the cookhouse gave it an appearance of translucency. The scene was the embodiment of Stillnacht that permeated one's senses. The only overriding sound was the shuddering of the shay as it built up excess steam at regular intervals.

This scene was so imbedded in my memory that every recollection of it elicits an emotional response. It was not until we rounded the trestle at the head of Voight Creek that I was aware of my physical presence. In retrospect, this incident seemed to represent a sort of allegorical gestalt that transcended the physical world into the spiritual one — a personal insight into the impermanence of an internal being that time obliterates.

Those Were The Days

My first glimpse of loggers at play was during the Pacific Logging Congress, which was held annually, and always at the Olympic Hotel in Seattle. This high rent area was part of the original land grant to the University of Washington and accounted for much of the building on the ever-expanding campus.

But back at the Olympic Hotel, the boys who fancied themselves as "brush apes," were indeed living it up for the long weekend. It was a time when the machinery companies found it expedient to wine and dine the timber gentry — a place to make those deals which netted them substantial profits in the sales of heavy equipment.

The most beautiful ballroom,

the Georgian Room, was always spoken for by the Caterpillar Tractor Company, where tables were loaded with gourmet food and bartenders with toothy smiles plied their wares at several locations. The bourgeois attendees seemed somewhat out of place in the splendor of crystal chandeliers, wall sconces and tapestries, but nobody seemed to care.

Certainly the most popular spot was the "sawdust bowl," a large room set aside for revelry and entertainment, which thrived during the late hours. Cases of expensive liquors were stashed in an adjoining storeroom so that those of Bacchus bent would never be in want. The steward of this supply suggested that the excess would be delivered to "deserving" participants on Sunday morning. Nothing functioned very efficiently the following week in the logging camps of Washington and Oregon.

The Western Forestry and Conservation Association hosted a more conservative group, notwithstanding that a fair sized contingent enjoyed a tippling bout and a measure of hi-jinx. Meetings alternated between Vancouver, Portland and San Francisco. It seemed that the more memorable ones were in the old Portland Hotel, a venerable edifice that resembled a medieval castle with old-world ambience.

It was there that a group of us were initiated into the "Boundary Busters." Actually, it was all nonsense and it had no known purpose or tenure, just an imaginative idea of a few young Turks. The only standard ritual was to down an old fashion barrel glass of Southern Comfort in one gulp. I do not remember all of the evening's rhetoric, but I did catch "Jake," our chief forester, pouring his glass into the pocket of J.A.K. Hall, who was standing next to him for the ritual toast. Hall was a most respected senior officer from the United States Forest Service at Madison, Wisconsin. To his credit, he never acknowledged any discomfort, thus spoiling the enjoyment of those on the know.

Our suite was always one of the turret corners in the hotel, where we could entertain after the day's deliberations. Jake knew everybody of note, as he spent many years in the U.S. Forest Service after graduating from the University of Minnesota in 1910. He loved to bait the government folks from Washington D.C. on their handling of timber sales and subsequent stewardship of public lands.

Always a favorite attraction each year, was the appearance of W. B. "Bush" Osborne, he of the Osborne Fire Finder, which is still used today in all the lookout stations. Bush always made his entry carrying a heavy pack sack which he emptied onto the largest dresser available. The many bottles were the makings for his famous dry Martinis and he loved to reign over the disbursements until the early hours. It was an unforgettable experience to see him perform with an old stocking cap and gloves with bells, together with his many smile creases and stories of woods experiences.

Invariably we would accumulate a coterie of Minnesota alums who identified closely with Jake, of course. Several times during the evening and early morning hours, one of these folks would stand on a chair and lead the Minnesota Rouser, which always elicited a loud cheer from the adherents of the maroon and gold, as well as those who became honorary alums on the spot. When the police arrived they were usually hooted down but cooler heads normally prevailed and the revelers eventually dispersed.

All was not voluntary chaos at these conventions because we did maintain a high degree of decorum during the meeting times and in the early evening. On one of our annual meetings held in San Francisco (always at the

Fairmont), our keynote speaker was the governor of California, Earl Warren. He made a big impression on the attendees because his speech contained what they wanted to hear, notably an affirmation of the conservative approach to timber use. It was later, when he was named to the Supreme Court, that a period of disenchantment began as Warren turned leftward.

One of the old timers we always looked forward to seeing at these conventions was Archie Whisnant, who, in later years, was a publisher of an Oregon forest journal. He would always be asked at some time in the proceedings to recite the tale of the "Baggage Car Behind," a poetic tear jerker of a railroad man bringing home his recently deceased wife. On every occasion when he finished, there was not a dry eye in the house. Remember, these were hardy folks and not prone to a display of feelings.

The nostalgia of these occasions is hard to dismiss. The memories of so many distinctive characters sometimes go through my mind like a passing parade. Yes, those were the days....

Behold,
The Tree Farm

It was the aftermath of the Great Depression and solvency was no longer the pressing problem. Lean years had trimmed the fat from both the woods and mill operations. One of my earliest jobs was to update the plat book of company fee lands and then evaluate those scattered portions that had almost reached their limit of tax delinquency. The policy set forth by Major Griggs was still in force, that of holding the land for growing in perpetuity.

Most of the parcels in question were logged during the 1890s and early 1900s. Those that were swampy or on poor growing sites because of high clay content, were easy to delineate — they would go back to the county. Much of the scattered areas of value were retained and sold to individuals at $10.00 per acre. A small amount down would negotiate a contract and most of the 10 to 40 acre parcels found a fairly ready market. We would see the value of this type of forest land go to $100.00 per acre in the next decade.

This was the time when we promoted slogans such as "Timber is a crop" and "We are a sustained yield company." We outlined our tree farm area of some 240,000 acres of fee controlled lands with detailed plans for its management, the parameters of same perceived as unlimited. St. Paul & Tacoma Lumber Company forestry and land administration consisted only of Norman Jacobson and myself. He gave me more or less free reign to ride off in several different directions according to where my enthusiasm would carry me. It was not long before I found myself tilting at

The Keep Washington Green committee is pictured here with the chairman, W. B. Greeley (second from left) and the author (to his left). From the author's collection.

windmills, as the limitations of corporate business and its attendant pragmatism tempered the grandiose plans. Nevertheless, it was an era of increased optimism in which Jake had the clout to convince management of a futuristic program that could keep us busy for many years to come.

We were able to keep the county assessor at bay with the threat of lands being taken off the tax rolls (St. Paul & Tacoma Lumber Company was the third largest taxpayer in Pierce County), so that the logged off-land valuations were kept at a modest level. Even in those days, it was evident that some day in the not too-distant future, we would be happy to evade the 12 1/2% yield tax. As a result, the company never did classify more lands under the Reforestation Act of 1931.

In the fall of 1940, I was given the monumental task of checking the reproduction on all of our logged-off lands, starting with those accessible to Camp One. My first night in camp turned out to be a memorable one as I was assigned to a bunkhouse with some hook tenders and chasers. They were uncommunicative compared to normal expectation, staring at the floor with folded hands for long periods of time. I did not understand this behavior until much later when it was evident that they tended to relive the working day and mull over the good and bad things they felt must be internalized.

After a time, one of my bunkmates suggested that I check my mattress. I did so and opined that it looked fine at the time. With that, he walked over and peeled back the heavy trim roll that the old time models had, exposing a regular raceway of bed bugs. There was a chorus of guffaws as I broke all records to chase down the bed maker for a replacement. By the time he arrived with a clean mattress, it was almost lights out — it was then that I noticed that all of the standard angle iron beds had a snoose can footing each leg. They were all filled with coal oil to form a bedbug-protective moat.

Living at Camp One brought back memories of my school days in 1929 as I noted a new crop of youngsters with lunch pails making their way up the hill to the one room schoolhouse. Dempsey Lumber Company had finished logging, but still had a manager on the job and their lands were easily accessible from C.C.C. roads built over our old railroad spurs from Camps One and Three.

Homesteads from the early days were easily spotted because the clearings were now filled with second growth almost big enough to be commercially valuable. Some of the old homestead cabins were still in fair shape, however, most of them had been burned or tumbled down from weathering with only a chimney remaining. One in particular, that of Baxter Robinson, could have been made livable with some minor repairs. His door and window openings were beautifully hand planed. It was evident that he had been an uncompromising workman. It was attested to by the old timers that he managed to bring in a piano back in the 1880s to give a touch of civilization to his claim.

Porter Brown, formerly camp steward and now railroad dispatcher, was a hulk of a man. He sat in a spindle-backed chair, which his ample frame overpowered and manned a schematic board of the entire company railroad system. The main lines and spurs were drilled at intervals to accommodate brass inserts marked with the locomotive and speeder numbers. As a unit was given the block, he would move the marker on and along the board while keeping track of all movements and shunting some traffic to sidings.

Porter spoke in a voice that was kind of a rumble and he liked to make fun of my mapping program. On several

The author (with hat) poses with (left to right) Harry Osborne, James Stevens, Billy Entwhistle and Bill Hagenstein (1941) in front of old stump around which grows second generation trees. The site marks the recovery of the area 16 years after a slash burn. From the author's collection.

occasions he waved his hand toward the windows and said "Those hills are as bare as a cat's ass and they won't grow trees again." He liked the bottle and was sometimes accused of having a voice slur, but never was he ever responsible for an accident due to negligence.

As a member of the team, Jake would see that I was able to attend the Western Forestry & Conservation Association meetings that were held annually. We shared a room that would always wind up as the headquarters for bull sessions and sometimes weighty deals would transpire

Allan Malcom is shown planting the "five millionth" tree on company lands in 1945. Looking on are E. G. "Spike" Griggs and W. D. Haggerstein. From the author's collection.

in the early morning hours. It was there that I met and became a disciple of E. T. Allen, who had become the elder statesman of western forestry, albeit a man without portfolio and proper respect due his national stature.

It was at one of these meetings during regular presentations that I had the temerity to try and change the prevailing practice of slash burning. My source of self-induced wisdom was a monograph by Thornton Munger, a career man in the forest sciences and highly placed in the U.S. Forest Service (Yale, class of 1910). His compelling study of slash burning versus no burning showed that the two curves from empirical evidence crossed at or near the four year mark. This study showing that land carried for four years lowered the fire risk to that of a successful slash burn fell on uncompromising ears. The state clearance from burned slash continued to carry more weight than the value of stored seed in the ground and surviving understory trees, not to mention the value of forest duff which served as a better substance for growth than the high potash residual from slash burning.

Nineteen forty was not a good year for fire prevention as Camp Five burned on July 1 at a time when woods operations were shut down for multiple vacations. When I had a chance to visit the area, it was heartbreaking to see the devastation. Only five resident bunkhouses on the lower end of camp had survived, one of which was later to become my temporary home. Not only was it a heavy loss for the company, but it also burned some Northern Pacific timber. Because it was alleged to be accidental from a short circuit in the auxiliary light plant, the company was spared punitive costs. We settled for a little over $14,000, based on a Porteous cruise of 1927.

In order to keep the woods operation going, we transported crews from Camp One, which was still operative. A new roof for the cookhouse at Camp Three was rushed to completion but it was decided that the rehab of the bunkhouses would prove too expensive and the project to work out of this camp was abandoned. It was only five and one half miles of additional transportation from Camp One to Camp Three and the prospect of rebuilding Camp Five within a reasonable length of time was also of prime consideration.

By 1941, we were dealing with Dempsey Lumber Company to buy all of their lands that were logged through

Camp One. It was because of the close relationship and goodwill we had with them that prompted Jim Dempsey to accede to a fairly modest closing price. This then became an important part of the company's tree farm in the Ohop area. Important in addition were the scattered homestead areas, which were well along in reproduction and provided a seed source for our lands, eliminating the need for tree planting.

Some incidental lands that had reverted to Pierce County through tax foreclosures were also on the market. Jake cleared a buying program with Spike Griggs, who gave us carte blanche to use our best judgement in the process. I was able to buy some uncontested lands that were within our control area, but some of them were bid up by locals who sometimes berated me for using the leverage of a large company to eliminate them in the bidding process.

Jake used his horse trading technique to negotiate some private sales to bolster our tree farm expansion plans. By the end of 1941 we had a total of over 140,000 acres of fee lands in the primary tree farm. The company controlled many more acres because of its favored position in both access and stewardship. Most of the Northern Pacific lands were bought together with their timber stands, the rest were placed under their subsidiary, the Northwest Improvement Company.

The year 1941 was a time when we started to become aware of what would later become a way of life, the salvage of logged-off land to recover values that had not been economically feasible before. Two of my former mentors while at the University of Washington, Fred Wangaard and O. Harry Shrader, agreed to team up with us for a comprehensive study of slash and residuals left behind in the normal course of logging.

We set up headquarters at Camp Two and spent

several weeks on random sampling of areas scattered throughout the Voight Creek Valley and the divide between Camps Two and Five. Results of this survey showed some definite values that could be recovered when small equipment and low overhead labor was made available. This study led to the extensive salvage program that I was to head several years later and which became too successful because it threatened those who managed a hostile takeover in the 1950s — too successful when the tail started to wag the dog. It did manage to reverse the dreams and projected plans of sustained yield and the game was, for all intents and purposes, over.

The author examines thinning from the Voight Creek Forest; the logs were destined for use in copper smelting operations in 1946. From the author's collection.

An Engineer's Life

Nearly everyone of our acquaintance remembers that fateful December 7 morning of 1941 when radio reports seemed preposterous, then the reality of the Japanese bombing of Pearl Harbor took over and questions of how an individual should handle it were pondered. In the weeks that followed, with Roosevelt's scornful excoriation of the Nipponese, we all were seeking the high ground to position ourselves where we could do the most good. Good friend Bill Price, of Weyerhaeuser Timber Company, was going into the army intelligence corps and thought he could check out a place for me because of my expertise in cartography, coupled with my R.O.T.C. training. "Cap'n

Bill" was mustered out sooner than he thought and nothing came of it.

Navy recruitment announced that they were looking for deck officers and it once again turned out to be a dead end. My below-par uncorrected vision could not be circum-navigated and it began to look like my services would come right after women and children. Ernie Allison asked Jake if he could transfer me into the logging department, where there was a desperate need for an engineer. The company immediately requested a classification of 2-A for me — "Registrants who are necessary or essential in their civilian activity." Although I never did serve overseas, the U.S. Coast Guard did accept me for service during the last year of the war.

Our woods operations did indeed need an engineer. My addition made a grand total of three, what with O. E. (Bud) Scharf as chief of crew, and Henry Beane as the grizzled veteran, we were hard put to keep up with logging department demands. It was a six day week, but more than that, it allowed for only 23 hours a week at home since we had to report to either Camp One or Electron Camp by 6:00 P.M. on Sunday nights.

It was apparent early on that Bud was not a full timer because he had to fill out reports ad infinitum and make special planning meetings. He also had an occasional bout with the bottle at inconvenient times. We could always tell when it was foreplanned, because we would get a full briefing before the weekend to take care of his absence on Monday. Our time was divided somewhat evenly between railroad layout and logging settings, which had to be contended with before the fallers and buckers could be sent in.

Each setting required running deflection lines to

establish boundaries for the falling process. In the canyon country we normally used a complicated yarding system called a "slack line." This required a special large drum on the yarder to accommodate a two-inch line that ran from an oversized block on the spar tree out to a tail spar, sometimes a high stump. The main line went through the carriage that ran on the slack line, allowing it to be raised or lowered to the choker setters who were often well below on the slope. The advantage of the slack line system was its reach, up to 2000 feet, and its ability to avoid hangups by getting just enough lift on the heavy line.

Our job as engineers was to run survey lines like the spokes of a wheel out from the head spar, meanwhile keeping a continuous profile of the terrain so that we could intelligently mark the safe distance that could be extended for yarding purposes. When all of these lines were run, we connected up the end points by blazing trees to give the fallers their cutting boundaries. These were important survey lines, or deflection lines, because it kept us in good rapport with the camp foreman. Loggers took a dim view of running lines over rocks or getting a dead hangup because of terrain.

Engineers had to keep well ahead of the logging because of selective or staggered settings, which meant a great deal of railroad main line and spur projection. Our first move into a new area required what we call "red carding," a preliminary line on a trial basis, which had to be changed according to the slopes and final destination. The use of red pasteboard markers, which showed up well in the timber, was the source for the name given. This rough "p" line was made using compass and abney level while the final alignment had to be more accurate with transit, steel tape and careful grade levels.

Before the construction crew came in we had to "bullfrog" it, that is, put in slope stakes. This was a job we did not like because it called for up and down the hillside all day putting in stakes where the cutting of the bank was to start. Each stake started with a guess, then had to be adjusted up or down to get the proper profile for the center line to be at the proper elevation.

During my years working as an engineer, the grade crew used a power shovel, which replaced the old steam shovel. Grade foremen used a "Swede level," or hand-held tube with crosshairs, which was used to sight high stakes marked with an adjustable short horizontal member adjusted to the height of the eye. Usually the shovel progressed on tracks that were supported on a flat bundle of squared-off timbers called a mat. This same sort of mat was also used to foot a spar tree that was to be raised at the landings.

In rock country there was no need to set slope stakes because it was just a matter of getting down to grade with enough side clearance to accommodate the width of the rail equipment. Good rock men were hard to come by. I worked with a true old timer when I was assigned alone on an engineering job near Mud Mountain Dam on the White River.

Our powder monkey on this job told a story about a big rock nose that he was assigned to blow on the Sunset Highway in Mount Rainier National Park. This one required the fracturing of the entire nose in one blast so that it could be mucked out with a power shovel. He bet the other workers that he could sit in a rocking chair on top of the rock outcrop undamaged when the charge went off. The men scrounged up an old rocking chair, and the betting was heavy both ways. When tons of powder were loaded into the T-shaped tunnel there was even more apprehension. The charge went off with a dull karrrrrump — the entire rock face lifted up only a few inches and then settled down, completed fractured. The old timer had a rough ride but stayed in the chair to collect his bet as promised. Heroes are made, not born.

When Camp Two burned on September 29, 1942, we had to make quick plans to continue somehow because of war demands. Luckily, the abandoned C.C.C. camp just off the county road at Electron was still in good shape and even had a cookhouse that was nearly operative. By October 15 this became our temporary camp. It was a long haul up to the logging operations, which by now were getting close to Rainier National Park. However, the accommodations were better than a normal camp and the access to civilization was most welcome.

One Monday evening, while we were in the Electron Camp, Nels Soderlind came over to our quarters and announced that a representative of the cadastral engineer's office from Washington D.C. would be around within the hour to interview us about names of physical features to be incorporated in the new quadrangle map due for publishing. This would be the official map for the region and the names would go down on the United States Geological Service quadrangle for all posterity.

On this occasion, Bud had once again failed to make it back to camp from one of his long weekends. There was just Henry and me. We did some powerful cogitating in fast order and decided that this was not the time to be evasive or vague. We quickly agreed on names that we thought appropriate or that in our view should be perpetuated.

Ernie Allison for sure, therefore, Allison Creek. Then, with proper respect for engineers of the past, we decided on H. G. Cowling (for a prominent ridge) and of course,

McGuire Creek for one of our alumni who had gone on to a job with the county. Charles Billings had to be remembered because he was our favorite cruiser, whose work was greatly detailed and accurate, to boot. About that time I became concerned that Henry might blurt out some of the more colorful names that we referred to in our survey books, such as the Pope's Nose and Cold Pecker Point.

In any event, all went well with our interview and the names we supplied did go on the official quadrangle map and appear there to this day. One creek did turn out to be a tribute to Henry, Beane Creek, because we had not taken it into account beforehand and he had to adhere to our agreement of full accord when I offered this to the representative. It was our introduction to the true meaning of ad hoc.

My association with Henry was a memorable and pleasant one. He was a bear of a man with a florid face and unwavering, upbeat disposition. For a person of his avoirdupois endowment, he could move pretty fast when the occasion demanded. Contrary to what many people believe, old growth forests are much more sterile for nearly all forms of wildlife than cut-over areas. Yellowjackets have never been advised of this and do thrive in ground holes deep in the forest primeval. They have a nasty habit of boiling out of the ground and up an engineer's pant leg when disturbed. It was quite a sight to see Henry run the 440 in record time after an encounter with these members of the hymenopterous order — yes, these too were memorable occasions.

There were desperate days in the employ of St. Paul & Tacoma Lumber Company. One that destroyed my semblance of dignity came at a time when Henry and I were marking U.S. Forest Service logs to separate them from our own. It had snowed overnight and the logs were badly jack-strawed. My bucket of fresco orange paint was nearly full when I slipped and upended it, emptying the contents on my head and over my new Filson jacket. When Henry found me he refrained from laughing, an act of restraint for which I felt grateful both at the time and in retrospect.

There was much more to humble the engineer. When in Camp Two, we always came back to a warm bunkhouse on Sunday nights. Not so in Camp Five on quite a few instances. True, we spent more time at Camp Two and the bullcook may not have been properly informed at Five. By the time we arrived on certain Sunday nights there was very little time before the light plant was turned off. We had to warm up our blankets by lamp light before we could put them back on our beds. One winter night, when I pulled the sheets apart, they gave off a distinctive crackling noise, the telltale sound of ice crystals.

It was while I was a logging engineer that a changing of the guard took place at the superintendent level. Ernie Allison was retired and as the most senior replacement waiting in the wings, Anton (Tony) Zoffel, was elevated to that position. (Nels Soderlind was too close to retirement himself.) Tony's experience with the company dated back to the 1920s when he was camp foreman of both Camps Six and Eight. Therefore he had the whiskers, as the saying goes. Tony epitomized the stereotype of "bull of the woods," much to the disappointment of many of the men who worked with him.

Superintendents are traditionally supposed to be up and about to see the crews off each morning. While at Camp Five it was not altogether uncommon to see Tony come out of his bunkhouse in the morning, grip the railing to keep his balance, then return without ever getting to the speeders.

Brother George, Camp Five foreman, was always there to cover for him. It was not until I became better acquainted with Tony that his basic problem became evident. He was very unsure of himself, and used drink to cover self doubts. Also, his uncertainty came out in the form of abuse when he dealt with the loggers. He was always polite to me, and on a one-to-one basis, was probably quite an acceptable person.

Before leaving the logging department to go back to the forestry and land section, we had acquired a new chief of party. Marc Titlow came to us from Weyerhaeuser Timber Company where he learned to run, not walk, to and from the job. He was quite a change from the laid back, if somewhat efficient, mode of life we had been used to. One day we were holed up in a watchman's shack for lunch, completely soaked to the skin, my teeth uncontrollably chattering from working in a driving sleet. Some of the bushelers were also there and one remarked, "Only a dirty dog would go out on a day like this." That was Marc's cue to say, "OK, lunch over. Let's get back to work."

Of Spoofs And Legends

When the early trappers and hunters of the northern woods came across tribes of Indians such as the Algonquins and Hurons, they were exposed to many legends and strange beliefs that piqued their interest. When visiting the lumber camps, these early pioneers found an interested group in the lumberjacks and so they interpreted the Indian lore into tall stories of exploits by woods personalities. Many a hunter and trapper found a good meal and bountiful drink among woodsmen to whom they expounded stories of great deeds, some of which found their way into the bunkhouse tales.

The Paul Bunyan legend actually belonged to the folklore emanating from the Lake States, not from the Far West. Most of the tales started in the shanty camps of Michigan and were recounted years later to Jim Stevens who, in turn, interested H. L. Mencken in the regeneration of this fabulous woods hero. It was not until 1925 that Jim published his original book on Paul Bunyan. It was his experience in working with several timber operations that inspired him to create such unforgettable characters as Hels Helson, Cream Puff Fatty, Johnny Inkslinger, Hot Biscuit Slim and Chris Crosshaulson. Along with Bunyan and his blue ox were tales of the winter of the blue snow, when the ground and horizon could not be distinguished — many manifestations of Stevens' fertile mind.

Although I had known Jim Stevens for many years, the foreword for his book as written by Stewart Holbrook had escaped my attention until much later. In Holbrook's words: "Stevens picked his Paul out of an old pile of Douglas fir slash he found in a clearing on the west slope of Mt. Rainier not far from Ohop." To which Jim added, "That's it! That's how it was." No more accurate description could be made of Camp One as I knew it in the 1920s. Letters addressed to residents of our base camp were: Camp One, Ohop, Washington. This, then, was Bunyan country.

Jim's last venture was a preparation for Disney Productions to introduce Paul Bunyan Jr. in cartoon form. On a visit to his home in Seattle, overlooking Lake Washington, he showed me many of the promotional drawings of young Paul and his woods friends — animals such as raccoons, beavers, chipmunks, etc., all in full color as produced by the Disney artists. Unfortunately, they did not survive the demise of the famous man himself, for Walt's successors opted to scrub the production.

Stewart Holbrook was clearly a legend in his own time as he was acknowledged the outstanding expert on early logging in America. A native of northern Vermont, he spent a large part of his youth in the nearby forests. He served with the army artillery during World War I and moved to the far west shortly after returning home. For several years, he scaled logs in the Pacific Northwest and later was on staff of the Lumber News in 1923.

Holbrook was author of eight books, the most famous of which was Holy Old Mackinaw. It was first published in 1938 and went through 19 printings by 1956. He created a rival to Paul Bunyan in the person of Jigger Jones, whose antics inspired readers to marvel at his strength and fortitude. Clad in bright vermillion underwear and with bare feet, Jigger Jones performed deeds that would be the envy of any lumberjack (Holbrook insisted upon using the term lumberjack long after it was considered out of touch).

Holbrook, in his later years, was busy on the lecture and steam-table circuit. Since after eating, many of the members of his audience tended to nod their heads, he used a ploy to get their full attention. Mixed in with his many slides he would place a picture of an attractive nude (most of the attendees were men). It was difficult to give much credence to his disclaimer of "How in the world did that get in there?"

Not all legendary folks were figments of the imagination. Back in the days of the river drivers on the Penobscot, Joe Peavey watched with interest an attempt to break up a big log jam. It was then that an idea came to him in a flash. He ran to the nearest blacksmith shop and directed the making of a prototype tool that was to revolutionize the life of the lumberjacks.

He fashioned a sort of short pike and cant dog combination, which employed a free swinging hook that was attached to a ferrule and allowed the sharp, tapered point to dog logs of varying size by closing the tool toward the pike at the end of the ferrule. This closing action gave a great deal of leverage to the tool, depending upon its length, and allowed the river drivers and mill jacks to roll logs in any desired direction.

This invention replaced swing dogs and became known as the peavey. Simply by reversing the leverage angle the peavey could be released, thereby saving the lives of many river driver who would have been rolled under maverick logs when they were caught in the torque of the immovable swing dogs. To this day, with only a few minor changes, the peavey has become a standard tool in the woods and on log decks.

Perhaps the greatest single testimony for the levity and light heartedness pervading loggers and lumbermen was the creation of the Hoo Hoo Club. There have been several interpretations as to how it all started, but a statement from its founder, Bolling Arthur Johnson, (he of the prodigious girth) is the only authentic one. In his words: "The Hoo Hoo Club started at 11 o'clock on the morning of January 21, 1892 while sitting on a lumber pile in Gurdon, Arkansas."

He was one of a group of lumbermen on the way to a convention in the South when their train was stalled in Gurdon. In order to while away the time, they broke out the bottles and commiserated with each other, the camaraderie ultimately leading to the need for an organization to continue their common bond. Johnson, together with four companions, first settled upon a name for the new group — "Ancient Order of Camp Followers."

After further reflection, it was decided that the connotation for this name was not quite what they wanted to project. Therefore, the suggestion by Adalbert Strauss that they adopt the name "Hoo Hoo," which had been coined by Bolling Arthur himself to make fun of a friend who had tied a few wisps of his hair into a top knot. The name of Hoo Hoo then became the generic for anything that was odd or unusual. A fanciful hand in poker became a Hoo Hoo hand, a new drink invented was a Hoo Hoo highball, and so on.

With an acceptable name, ideas were bandied about for a logo that would accompany the organization in the

The famous "Hoo Hoo" Club founder, Bolling Arthur Johnson, is pictured on the right. The fraternal organization of timber harvesters was founded in 1892. To his right is George Cornwall, editor of The Timberman Magazine. Photo courtesy The Tacoma Public Library.

rituals, badges, etc. The notion of the cat whose traditions dated back to ancient Egypt was most intriguing, particularly since it purported to have nine lives, which could be transferred to the number of officers and also invoke the mysteries of the Pharaohs as an adjunct. It was decided that the proper name should be the Concatenated Order of Hoo Hoo and one member, W. E. Barnes, volunteered that names could be derived for the officers from the Lewis Carroll books.

From Alice Through the Looking Glass came the Bandersnatch and the Jabberwock; from The Hunting of the Snark came the Boojum and the top man in the person of the Snark himself. The actual quotation from Carroll went like this:

> *"In the midst of the word he was trying to say,*
> *In the midst of his laughter and glee,*
> *He had softly and suddenly vanished away —*
> *For the Snark was the Boojum, you see."*

The symbol adopted was the black cat, in which all superstition was denied. It came about because a large black cat came into the room where the lumbermen were gathered for an organizational meeting and proceeded to make itself at home. It was an omen not to be denied and all felt that providence played into their hands.

To round out the nine officers of this unholy academy, it was decided that a Junior and Senior Hoo were appropriate, then Gurdon, of course, to commemorate the place where it all started. The list was filled out to include the Arcanoper, Scrivenoter and Custocatian. At first, the head of the several chapters was called the Grand Snark, but later this was considered too conventional, so they came up with the humble name of Snark of the Universe.

And so it was that the organization prospered and the black cat was seen throughout the land. Each lapel pin had the member's sequential number inscribed on the back. My father had a fairly low number, but when I joined in 1944 we were up to 49,143. I served on the initiation or concatenation team as Jabberwock, wearing my black robe and peaked hat to solemnize the occasion.

The Hoos Hoos had quite a number of poems written about them. However, one that appeared seemed to best epitomize the flavor of the organization. It went like this:

> *Oh, the Great Black Cat has a high old time*
> *As it yowls and screams in reckless rhyme.*
> *It fears no owls to who! to who!*
> *For brave is the cat of the great Hoo Hoo.*
>
> *It stealeth along o'er the cottage thatch*
> *And winketh its eye at the Bandersnatch,*
> *As he goeth abroad on mischief bent,*
> *Or cometh in late, somewhat crapulent.*
>
> *It's out for a night on a regular lark*
> *And it tickles the nose of the sleeping Snark,*
> *Who smiles as he dreams the Black Cat's kiss*
> *Was a favor received from a loving miss.*

Loggers and lumbermen were a hard working sort, but it was axiomatic that those who worked the hardest also played the hardest. They were particularly vulnerable to the notion that Paul Bunyan and his likes were role models whom they never cared to disavow. The era of big trees, big machines and grandiose ideas served as the overtone to the tales that emanated from the early bunkhouses.

The Great Black Cat, symbol adopted by the Hoo Hoo Club.

The Twilight Years

For nearly a year my permanent home was Camp Five. One of the old bunkhouses that survived the fire of 1940 was remodeled and I had the crew take our cherry picker and attach another one at right angles so that it ended up as a two level house. About that time, Spike and Mary Lea Griggs built a new summer home just below us on the old siding spur, which was not very short of luxurious.

The company built a light plant and garage unit so that we had reliable AC electricity for lights and appliances, also a large propane tank for stove and heater use. We took turns starting the light plant at dusk and then shutting it down later in the evening. The signal to warn the others of a shutdown was three flips of the master switch, then a wait of five minutes.

Spike was an avid fisherman, albeit a purist, eschewing all lures other than a dry fly. In later years, we often took their Jeep up to the Golden Lakes in the national park or to where we could walk into two fine fishing lakes on company property. Both Spike and Mary Lea had their own small rubber raft well hidden and I had to take a solemn oath never to divulge where they were. On some weekends we would have a cookout to include the Zoffels, who had retained the remaining two bunkhouses at old Camp Five.

Mary Lea was an activist in all matters of forestry and pragmatic conservation, the latter in contrast to the doomsdayers who were just starting to be heard. She spearheaded a national movement to deter the adoption of Smokey Bear as the symbol of the U.S. Forest Service. Bears are destructive in the woods, particularly in the second growth where they strip the bark for the sweet sap at the cambium layer. It was a futile battle as Smokey Bear was adopted in 1943, with ranger hat and shovel to give credence to forest fire awareness.

Back on the farm — tree farm that is — progressive plans that had been on hold during the war started to once again develop. Our planting program to rehab the large area of burned slashed in the 1942 fire was heading the list. The big push came from 1944 to 1946, when we reached the 8 1/2 million mark of planted trees, mostly Douglas fir. I personally planted several thousand. Some day the woods crew logging in the second growth will wonder why there is such a neat row of noble firs (Abies genera) running down some of the section lines.

We did most of our planting with high school boys

who were quite a conscientious lot for the most part, but needing constant supervision to control their hi-jinks. Jake wanted a small crew of men to fill in some of the gaps where transportation was a problem. We spotted a bunkhouse on the Camp Two main line and remodeled it to house a cook and crew of eight. One day a sign appeared placed neatly on a post (later found to be a Marc Titlow artifact) that read — Stierville. Although it did not last long, the name stuck and it was the nucleus of some local jokes for months to come.

In order to get transportation when needed on the railroad, the company assigned me a speeder that carried the commercial name of Casey Jones. Its model-T motor was a difficult one to start, so I often pushed the speeder onto the main line and let it drift downhill until the motor caught. The track gang put in a siding for me just below the old Bootlegger Crossing so I had a permanent place to park.

With the end of the war, the Wilkeson Coal & Coke Company, a St. Paul & Tacoma Lumber Company subsidiary, never reopened the mines and developed the coal reserves near Wilkeson and Carbonado. Their office space then reverted to the forestry department and gave us a much better base to work from. Coal deposits were fair game in the war years and like many other prospective adjuncts to the war effort, the high sulfur content and rehabilitation costs proved too great a barrier to overcome.

It had been an interesting era in the 1880s when the timber consignment was first made by the Northern Pacific Railway Company. They had reserved the mineral rights on 4160 acres in order to accommodate a partnership of four that operated under the name of Carbon Hill Coal Company. The identities of the four partners was of greater import at a later date when they were revealed to be Charles Crocker,

Leland Stanford, Collis Huntington and Mark Hopkins. Mineral rights on their land reverted back to St. Paul & Tacoma Lumber Company and in turn to the Wilkeson Coal & Coke Company, which developed some interest during the time of Major Griggs.

In the early days, other coal operations were also only mildly successful. The Tacoma Smelting Company bought lands in the Fairfax area along the Carbon River with prospects of copper and other metals. One of our railroad spurs was named after the Montezuma mine, which played out without any real results. We opened up the entire mining claim area to roads in the early 1940s and established the Montezuma gate and gate house to control access. Permanent resident houses were also built at the sites of the King Creek and Voight Creek gates. By this time, the tree farm boundaries had been established to encompass 240,000 acres, much of which was in fee simple ownership.

It was becoming more and more evident that the logging personnel were changing to fit the new conditions of timber harvesting. Camp Two was accessible by trail from the Mowich Lake State road and Camp Five, later Camp Seven, had an isolation that the new breed of loggers were shunning. Thus it was that the number of "stumpers" gradually increased — those who lived at home and drove their cars to Camp One to be picked up by speeder, or those who parked along the Mowich Lake road and walked down into Camp Two.

Looking back to the early logging days, it did indeed resemble a full-circle process. At that time, operations were closer to what was then civilization and those that opted to live in camp could, more often than not, set up quarters for their wives in a cabin of their own. The big change over the years was, of course, the job classifications. Bull whackers, swampers, whistle punks, hair pounders, pot punchers and scissorbills (anyone who was a contra-Wobbly) had long since disappeared. They were replaced by another group who, in turn, was destined to become part of the lexicon of antiquity at the end of the steam age. They were the bullcooks, trackwalkers, donkey punchers, pit men, gandy dancers, flunkeys, high climbers, iron burners and roustabouts.

A lament to the passing of an era is not the intent of this book, nor is succumbing to nostalgia a preferred choice. The St. Paul & Tacoma Lumber Company forestry policy certainly belied this, particularly in the 1940s. It was the loss of momentum that is deplored, together with an attendant increase in the number of checks and balances, hence the notion of the twilight years.

When Bent Gerdes walked into my office looking for a position in our department, he had a sympathetic ear. It seemed so incongruous that a fellow with a master's degree in forest management would be spending his time in our mill on the green chain. For Jake, Gerdes was an anomaly because Jake was suspicious of "foreigners," but in the end a scenario in which Gerdes could spearhead an innovative program for us did win out. Jake always had an open mind if he could see a public relation opportunity.

What followed was more of a tribute to the aspirations of what Gerdes felt was the way to go — I was merely the means to carry them out. My first introduction to what genetics could mean to the future of forest management started with him. Together we searched for elite trees, those that had the best growth characteristics, with shape and color of secondary consideration. Gerdes used a shotgun to knock off branch sections, which we used as scions for grafting to small second-growth trees. We never were able to follow up on seed production, etc. but I often wondered how much mystery our small grove of unusual trees would cause some time in the future.

We were able to improve our planting techniques and seed selection with our Danish forester leading the way. Perhaps the most important contribution he made was to select trees to be thinned, a job that I had always done myself with different priorities. The effects of proper thinning would be carried on until the time of ultimate harvest. Gerdes went on to eventually run his own business in which he used to advantage his particular penchant as an entrepreneur.

Evidently the company heads thought my handling of production within the department looked promising. I was gradually nudged into a salvage and prelogging activity with gyppo (contract) loggers. At first we did business pretty much on a handshake, and more or less out of the hip pocket, as the saying goes. When it became necessary to draw up contracts, some of the gyppos showed a great deal of resentment, feeling that they were not to be trusted.

For several years the law firm of Grosscup, Morrow and Ambler had been making inroads into the business and found more and more reasons to control things, first with the accounting department, and then into management itself. Like the camel nosing into the desert tent, they soon became very much part of the act, in fact were able to create the aura of the indispensable.

All attempts at innovation for further utilization of the salvage potential were met with caution signs. It was clear that fear of litigation was starting to dictate company policy in all contract dealings, and even with our own personnel. One day Spike sent me to the legal eagle's Seattle office to get final approval on a contract. After waiting an appropriate time to ensure proper respect, I was ushered into Ben Grosscup's plush office.

Ben was a portly man who was able to cover a measure of disdain with an attempt at affability. I made the mistake of trying out some new ideas on him after he made the necessary changes in the contract. This experience was much like working one's way through a maze where every turn brings up another barrier. With an attitude that could only be construed as impatient tolerance, he as much as told me to stay away from all attempts at decision making.

This phenomenon of decision constriction was working its way at all levels. It was difficult to see Jake finding out that his entire format of conducting business, one of directness and simplicity, based on personal logic, was being molded into a ponderous process of rating and approval at the highest executive level. He had always been able to make salutary decisions in the company interest, later backed up, if necessary, by the Major or Spike Griggs.

For me, it was a difficult row to hoe. It had always been taken for granted that we would roughly outline our projects and then leave the details for me to carry out. Jake had always been my backstop, albeit requiring some back-filling at times, but it was the sort of arrangement that made for a progressive program. He became morose at times and it was apparent that his health was being affected by loss of clout. The gradual diminution of power was coupled to his eventual demise in my opinion. Jake was a product of the Old West and could neither understand or assimilate the increased accountability, unfortunately leading ultimately to a world of clandestine intrigue and duplicity. As my mentor, so also was he my indoctrinator, and I ultimately went the way of the disenchanted.

Perhaps the greatest loss to the timber industry as corporate giants got bigger was the degradation of spontaneity; caution replacing candor. It was a subtle misdirection of the Western spirit of grandness that had created strong economic opportunities in the forest, and men who believed in their ability to manage their destiny with open arms and hearts.

For Want Of A Dollar

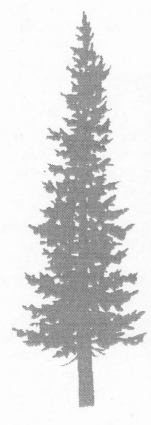

When Major Griggs announced the building of the Union Bag and Paper Company plant in Tacoma on September 1 of 1927, he was meeting the problem of increased Hemlock production head on. The pulp plant was to use the kraft or sulphate process and could handle some Douglas fir and Abies fir as well as hemlock and spruce in the 120-ton plant. The lumber company could develop 150,000 board feet of hemlock to supply this plant on a continuum, the import of which was greatly appreciated at the time. It was really the start of the Griggs expansion program which he did not live to see carried out.

Nooksack operations in Whatcom County were important to

continuity, but only in a tangential fashion. Logs produced there were destined for tidewater in the Bellingham area and were sorted there for the most part. This operation was shut down during the Great Depression and only restarted in the 1940s, when additional timber was purchased and farmed out to contractors.

The Depression years sounded the death knell for the Union Bag and Paper Company as the plant was shut down in 1932. It would have been the ideal appropriation for St. Paul & Tacoma Lumber Company because of its contiguous property adjacent to the milling operation. The billions of pulpable timber by board foot measure were there to back it up, both in fee lands and controlled lands. In any event, it was St. Regis Paper Company that was able to swing the deal as they opened up a rejuvenated plant in 1936.

Soon after the war, Olympia Veneer Company was unable to sustain its plywood operation for lack of timber supply and sold out to St. Paul & Tacoma Lumber Company. At the time, this was a definite plus because the company still had years of peelable Douglas fir, albeit in somewhat diminishing supply. As it turned out later, it was not the bonanza intended as the company had to buy an increasing amount of peeler blocks on the open market. What is more significant, in my opinion, is that the need for Douglas fir old growth forced the company's hand into making decisions and deals that ultimately started an unravelling process.

Spike Griggs' most embarrassing moment, according to his accounting, was on the occasion when he was to introduce Teddy Roosevelt as the honored speaker at the Tacoma Lumberman's Club. The affair was held in the crystal ballroom of the Winthrop Hotel and Spike wanted to inject a combination of humility and humor into his effort.

Being familiar and somewhat enamored with railroading, he prefaced his formal introduction by saying, "I feel like a mallet pushing a boxcar out on the main line."

There was a sustained silence as the attendees failed to grasp the metaphorically reversed intent. After a great deal of lip licking, Spike tried to explain that the mallet was indeed the intended prime mover and the boxcar only the foil. From that point on he managed to recover some decorum and Teddy never acknowledged any impropriety.

The true embarrassing incident should have come many years later when we were being forced to find additional lower-elevation timber to sustain the plywood mill, and to some extent, select grades of Douglas fir in the mill. There were hints that Kosmos Timber Company, whose fee lands were intermingled with those of the U.S. Forest Service, was possibly on the market.

Spike set up a preliminary exploration of these lands and early one August morning I dropped him and Cordy Wagner off at the head of the drainage area, picking them up in early evening miles down-country. They were both very enthusiastic with what they were able to see and agreed to follow up on their expectations.

It all started with a clandestine meeting in the little town of Randle, Washington, where five of the top timber cruisers from west of the Cascades met with Jake to implement this secret project. We set up headquarters in an obscure motel and proceeded to start the crash program.

We had the help of a "mole" in the person of Jack Sutherland, superintendent of Kosmos Timber Company, who still held some allegiance to St. Paul & Tacoma Lumber Company from his earlier days. Of course, there were some implied rewards, such as the hint of a top job for services rendered.

We had our cruisers working seven days a week for two weeks in order make the time limit given to us. Jack Sutherland wanted to make his contacts with us very secretive. However, he always arrived each evening in a cloud of dust in his very conspicuous, big white Lincoln.

My job was to compile all of the cruising data and put it in standard form. We were able to rush this information back to the Tacoma office after the two-week stint. Spike then wrote a letter of intent and tender offer to Bob Fox, owner/manager of Kosmos Timber Company's lands and operations.

When we heard that the offer was accepted it was a time of elation, not knowing at the time that the other shoe was about to drop. I did not find out until much later, proceedings being hushed up, what the extent of the problem would prove to be.

Our main vault was filled with legal documents that bore the time honored preamble: "For the sum of one dollar paid in hand and other valuable considerations...." It was standard practice to conform to legal protocol by acknowledging the transfer of tender (one dollar being significant) as a binder to a sales agreement.

The actual amount of the sale in monetary terms was felt to be a private concern, hence the use of "other valuable considerations" nearly always stipulated an amount of money carried in a separate instrument. Revenue stamps on the original document would give away the actual amount to a curious person. However, the registered form carried in the county office did not list the revenue amount.

In any event, the secret leaked out that Spike had failed to include any payment in hand, which made the enforcement of the provisions invalid if the seller so wished. Bob Fox had second thoughts and decided to hold his property for a better offer. He ultimately sold out to the U.S. Plywood Company, where he was able to realize a better deal through stock options.

In my opinion, this was the turning point of the company's destiny as we had to move on to the next consideration — one that unknowingly led to the ultimate dismantling of the tree farm as we knew it and to the very well-being of St. Paul & Tacoma Lumber Company.

Hilding Lindberg had come on the scene back in 1931, when his wholesale grocery company made an offer to run the cookhouses for St. Paul & Tacoma Lumber Company camps. While his offer was turned down, Hilding did run cookhouses for other companies, and he worked his way into logging operations for St. Paul and teamed up with Frank Hobi to form a partnership that was to last for years. Hilding formed the Ladd Logging Company with holdings near Morton, Washington.

It was Ladd that St. Paul & Tacoma Lumber Company bought instead of Kosmos Timber Company, more of a stop gap than a true investment in the future. During several planning meetings, I had a chance to observe Hilding Lindberg, an ambitious man who eventually gained control of the company's destiny. Spike Griggs, as president of the C. W. Griggs Investment Company with 53% of the stock, had been able to ensure continuity of the old guard at St. Paul & Tacoma Lumber Company through the years because the various stockholders within the group were remnants of the company founders. In the end, it was Chauncey Griggs who played the pivotal role in surrendering to the maverick Lindberg group.

The disposition later of St. Paul & Tacoma Lumber Company into the hands of St. Regis Paper Company extends beyond the scope of this book. Needless to say, it was difficult to see Spike Griggs being sent out to pasture, along with the dynamic Corydon Wagner. A new group was to move in, and the familiar gray office building at 1220 St. Paul Avenue was never the same again.

Perhaps it was a fitting way to bring down the curtain. My grandfather tended the horse barn soon after Mill A went into production in 1889. My father started out as water boy for the mill hands in 1909 and went on to become the accounting department manager. My time in the tall timber was as rewarding as one could ask. It was only when the challenge and the enjoyment were removed in disappointing increments that I chose to move on. This is the way of all things impermanent, however. St. Paul & Tacoma Lumber Company will always be my ancestral heritage, even as the name faded away like the lumberjacks in the annals of woods lore.

In retrospect, there are random memories of my years in the woods that surface from time to time, during that nether-world of reverie which precedes sleep. I am once again walking on the soft forest floor, observing the cathedral-like aspects of the big timber. Sometimes it reflects in the musty odor of the conks on old windfalls, sometimes on the balsam perfume of the upland Abies. It may be the drumming of a roughed grouse, which increases in tempo until fading out; perhaps a startled deer who first stomps the ground, then runs off at top speed.

It is a kaleidoscope of people who made up the faces that fit into the scheme of things — Perry Silvernail, my road construction genius, for whom the past tense of "reach" was "retch"; old Peter, the "swamp angel" whose flowing white beard was a familiar sight on the Carbon River Road, and of course, Henry Beane, with his rustic wisdom regarding human frailties.

Random thoughts always include such things as the winter nights when I had to make my barefoot way from the bunkhouse to the lavatory over wood planking thoroughly scarified by cork shoes; the early mornings when the bullcook came in to light up the pot bellied stove; the dampening of noises during a soft snowfall and the warm air rushing out of the cookhouses carrying odors of bacon and coffee. It all fits somewhere in the pattern of a shadowy past, then disappears with the light of a new day.

The last train load of logs in 1949 was a poignant occasion for the author who, with Nels Soderlind and Bill Hoffman, looks on as the the Twelve-Spot, with three gondolas and skeleton cars, prepares to get under way. From the author's collection.

Epilogue

The decision to convert to truck logging was made in the fall of 1948. There ensued the usual feasibility study but nobody doubted that the saga of steam logging was about to enter its final stage, the last chapter. Camp Seven, still new and destined to be the last of its kind, was to become the terminus of the main road with Lake Kapowsin as the point of departure. Indeed, the die was cast.

Camp Two was shut down on September 9, 1949 and logs were starting to come down the Mowich Lake Road by truck just three days later. It was the last week in August when I got wind of the final trip by rail for logs to come out of the company operations. The lump in my throat at the finality of it all was not shared by others. It was up to me to get a photographer on the scene to record the event for posterity. This was the last time I would see Nels Soderlind on the job. He retired soon after.

As an event of such import, it was not impressive. The last load consisted of three flats and three gondolas, the latter loaded with chunks and some short, scabby logs, a far cry from the long trains of the past. We were down to three locomotives, the 12-spot being given the honor to bring down the cars to the interchange, the Two-spot following solo on its way to the boneyard. I met Nels and side rod Bill Hoffman, a mile below Camp Two where we set up for the last look.

I recalled the dust cover of a Saroyan novel that pictured a small boy waving at a passing locomotive. The engineer waved back, and it was apparent without opening the book that this event happened at regular intervals. The engineer indulged the boy and the boy pursued his dreams as the air must have been filled with the distinctive odor of escaping steam tinged with cylinder oil.

It was like that here. I waved and the engineer waved back. The shay continued on down the main line and slowly disappeared around the bend. The passing of an era, one that was never to return. A realization that only a handful really cared prompted a particular feeling of emptiness. I hoped that a last wave of the hand would not be lost in oblivion. Somebody needed to tell the story.

References

Carroll, Lewis, *The Hunting of the Snark,* Pantheon Books, 1966.

Defebaugh, James, *History of the Lumber Industry of America,* The American Lumberman, 1907.

Greeley, William, *Forests and Men,* Doubleday & Company, 1951.

Holbrook, Stewart, *Holy Old Mackinaw,* Macmillan Company, 1938.

Holbrook, Stewart, *Prophet of Forestry,* Weyerhaeuser News #31, February, 1956.

McCulloch, Walter, *Woods Words,* The Oregon Historical Society and Champoeg Press, 1958.

Morgan, Murray, *The Mill on the Boot,* University of Washington Press, 1982.

Stevens, James, *Paul Bunyan,* Alfred A. Knopt, 1925.

Tacoma Daily Ledger, January 1, 1890.

The Loggers, Time-Life Books, 1976.

Western Writers of America, *Trails of the Iron Horse,* Doubleday & Company, 1975.

Glossary Of Woods Terms

Adverse	Reference to a grade for an uphill haul.
Axle grease	Term for butter in the cookhouse.
Back forty	Any place away from the main activity.
Back guy	Guy line on a spar away from the yarding direction.
Bagley	A dragline system to move earth for cuts and fills.
Bald face	Pushing a car rather than pulling on the railroad.
Ballast	Gravel used to support railroad ties.
Banana belt	Low altitude logging operation.
Barber chair	A tree which splits upward along the grain during the falling process.
Barkie	A pole sold with the bark still on.
Base line	Starting line for a survey, usually township line.
Bastard	An off breed — something that does not fit.
Batter pile	Piling driven at an angle to give inward strength in trestle construction.
Bearing tree	A tree marked to reference a survey corner.
Bedmaker	Maker of beds who stores mattresses, etc. in camp.
Bell	Sliding socket used to secure a choker around a log.
Bent	Set of piles in a trestle.
Bicycle	Travelling unit used on a skyline to accommodate chokers (see Carriage).

Bight	Loop in a wire rope.
Binder	Chain or wire rope (sometimes a combination) to keep logs in place during transportation.
Blaze	Axe mark on a tree to designate a boundary on survey.
Block	A sheave rotating in a casing to carry wire rope — constructed like a pulley.
Blowdown	Trees or snags blown down by the wind.
Blue top	A stake where the top is flush with the grade level — often marked with blue keel.
Board foot	The equivalent of 144 cubic inches of wood.
Board up	The action of cutting successive notches in a tree butt to reach the correct height for a springboard.
Bobcat	Cat yarding without an arch or pan.
Boneyard	Yard where equipment is stored until disposed of
Boomer	An employee for a short time only.
Boom stick	Long log with chain holes drilled in both ends to contain loose logs in a pond or river.
Brakie	A brakeman on the railroad.
Brand	An indented impression made by an embossing hammer to identify owner- ship in logs.
Brier	Another name for a crosscut saw.
Broomtail	A horse used in logging.
Brow log	A large log at the landing site to keep logs off the track and up to near the loading height.
Brush ape	Name that a logger calls himself.
Buck	Act of cutting logs to length.
Buckle guy	A guy line to keep spar trees from bending near the middle.

Bull block	The mainline block near the top of a spar tree.
Bull bucker	Man who controls falling and bucking — keeper of records for bushelers.
Bullcook	Camp employee who cleans bunkhouses, builds fires, etc.
Bullfrog	Traveling up and down the hillside to put in slope stakes for the grading crew.
Bullhead	A timber wider at one end than the other.
Bull of the woods	Camp foreman or superintendent who is seen to be tougher than usual.
Bull puncher	Also "whacker" — ox team driver.
Bull tram	Locking the tracks of a bulldozer with a wrap of wire rope to get positive traction.
Bunk log	Logs on the bottom outside of a load of logs.
Busheler	A faller or bucker paid on a piece work basis.
Butt rigging	Swivel system attaching chokers to the mainline and haulback — (see Jewelry).
Butterfly hook	Type of choker hook that has a closing flange which locks into place.
Cabin fever	A logger who loses control of his actions because of being alone (bunkhouse term — "wring ass").
Calks	Tapered nails fastened to shoe bottoms, normally screw threaded — later called "corks."
Cant hook	Short handled peavey without a pike end.
Car spotter	Auxiliary drum on a yarder that is attached to railroad cars for pulling into place to be loaded.
Carriage	Large double-sheaved unit that rides on the skyline where the main and haulback lines control the chokers.

Cat skinner	Bulldozer operator, either earth moving or log yarding.
Chain	Early measuring unit of surveys — 66 feet in length — (80 chains = 1 mile).
Chaser	Man who unhooks the chokers from the logs at a landing.
Cherry picker	A vehicle with a boom for picking up things with a wire rope drum.
Choker	Wire rope section with ferrules to attach logs to the yarding line.
Choker setter	Member of a crew who attached chokers around logs to the butt rigging.
Cold deck	Logs piled up to be brought into a landing later on.
Comealong	A wire rope connection temporarily attached to the main line or haulback.
Conks	Fruiting bodies of fungus in rotting wood.
Cookee	Old term for second cook, also used for a flunkey.
Coyote hole	Larger than normal hole for placing a powder charge.
Cribbing	Logs piled up at right angles to replace piling.
Crosshaul	Logs rolled with a pull on a bight at right angles to the log — (also called parbuckle).
Crotch line	Method of loading logs with single tongs at each end of the log — (sometimes with spreader bar).
Cruiser	Estimator of timber volume from sampling standing trees.
Crummy	Early term for a logger's bed roll and possessions — also a railroad caboose, later for a small closed car.

d.b.h.	Diameter at breast height of a tree — about 4 1/2 feet above ground level.
Deacon seat	Bench running the length of an old bunkhouse, usually in front of the bunks.
Dehorn	Person who drinks any alcohol, often cookhouse extracts.
Derail	Switch that sends railroad runaways down a gravel bed as a safety measure.
Dog	Action of blocking any movement — also a pawl to hold a toothed wheel in place.
Donkey	Multiple drum machine for yarding logs.
Dragline	System of hauling in a bucket filled with earth or ballast with wire rope (see Bagley).
Drawhead	Coupling device between railroad cars.
Drip torch	Devise to start slash fires by tilting applicator.
Dummy tree	A tree used to help raise a spar tree in place.
Dutchman	On the railroad, a replacement rail section — in logging, a block to change direction of haul.
Fall block	A block lowered in the bight of a line.
Fire in the hole!	Powder monkey's cry of warning to clear the area before blasting.
Flunkey	Waiter or waitress in the cookhouse.
Fresno	An early dragline system using wheels.
Friction blocks	Hardwood blocks that work like an engaging clutch — a safety factor on hangups.
Frog	The unit used in railroading to switch from one track to another — section of rail with switch points.
Flying	The number of chokers on any given turn, e.g., flying three chokers.
Gandy dancer	Track maintenance worker.

Gin pole	Single pole set at an angle with block used for loading logs or miscellaneous items.
Gondola	Standard length railroad car with steel sides and ends.
Gopher hole	Hole blown under a log to allow a choker to pass through — also a small coyote hole for blasting.
Grease monkey	In the old days, the man who greased skids — later, one working with machinery maintenance.
Ground lead	Yarding logs directly from the drum level.
Gun	The act of lining up a tree undercut to sight along its fall direction with an axe — also name for a woods transit.
Gut hammer	Iron rod used on a triangle to announce that camp meals are ready in the cookhouse.
Guy	A wire rope shackled to a spar tree and tail hold to keep the spar upright and in place.
Gyppo	A contract logger or truck driver.
Gypsy	Name given to a vertical spool (drum) used in the early days of ground lead.
Hair pounder	A horse or mule driver.
Hangup	Term to indicate an impediment to logs being yarded.
Haulback	Return line to bring chokers back to the setters.
Haywire	Light wire rope used to haul heavy lines or blocks in place (see Straw Line) — also a snafu operation.
Hayrack	Loading boom using two parallel poles — McLean type of loading boom used after the turn of the century.
Head block	Same as bull block i.e., main line block.

Heel boom	Loading boom where pressure is used near the base to lift the heavier end of the log.
Heel tackle	Line and block system to tighten the skyline — normally used on a skidder.
Hiyu	Chinook jargon for "plenty."
High climber	Logger who limbs and tops a tree to be used as a spar for high lead or skyline.
High lead	Often spelled Hi-lead. Any system using a head spar but no tail spar.
Hook tender	Also called a "hooker" — a man in charge of the yarding crew and releasing chokers at the landing.
Hoot owl	Early shift to complete work before the humidity drops to the danger level.
Hot deck	Landing where logs are loaded soon after yarding — opposite of cold deck.
Hyas	Chinook jargon meaning "something good" "or works well."
Iron burner	Blacksmith.
Jacob staff	Staff with swivel head and pointed ferrule base to support a compass — a "Jake" staff.
Jerk wire	Wire attached to a yarder for the whistle punk to signal instructions — used in the "old days" only.
Jewelry	Name given to the butt rigging.
Jillpoke	Any pole or member used to jam against something to hold it in place — also a sort of shear to unload logs.
Jim Crow	A one-log load — usually bunked in place by two small logs.
John D	Coal oil or kerosene — also a term for a busheler's oil bottle fitted with a hook.

Johnson bar	Lever used to reverse direction of an engine; used on locomotives and some bulldozers.
Jump-up skid	Ramp logs placed next to loading area for parbuckling logs onto cars.
Landing	Place where logs are brought in from the woods.
Lang lay	Wire rope where the strands are twisted in the same direction to give more flexibility.
Lead block	(old term) Block with wide sheave to allow butt rigging to pass through — (see Tommy Moore).
Line	Wire rope — either wire or hemp center.
Line horse	Horse used in the early days to pull the yarding line back out to the woods.
Live reel	Reel of hose for fighting fire kept under pressure.
Loading pot	Small donkey used for loading only.
Logger's dream	Portable logging unit for fast yarding of small timber — uses direct drive.
Logging chance	An operating area — same as logging "show."
Long splice	Splice made in lines where it must withstand a heavy pull.
Luff	Set of blocks to give the maximum lift or pull.
Marlin spike	Somewhat like a sailor's spike but longer taper — used in splicing line.
Mat	Short lengths of logs bundled together to form a base for a raised tree or as a base for heavy equipment.
Misery whip	Also called a misery "harp" i.e., old-style cross cut.
Molly Hogan	Single strand of wire rope woven into circular form for a temporary splice.

Moonbeam	Guide used at the base of a pile driver to hold batter piles in place while driving.
Mop up	Term used for putting out hot spots in fire fighting.
Muck stick	A shovel, normally a Number 2.
Mud cap	Method of tamping in a powder charge using clay or mud.
Mulligan car	Car used to bring lunch out to logging sites in early days — later called a Crummy.
P-line	Preliminary survey line.
Pack rat	Large rat with bushy tail resembling a squirrel — habitually trades objects for those taken.
Pan skid	Metal pan with front end curved upward to keep logs from digging in — used in bulldozer yarding.
Parbuckle	Old method of loading logs by rolling them onto cars by pulling both ends of a bight — (see "Crosshaul").
Pass block	Small block hung near the top of a spar tree to haul up heavier blocks or tree jacks, etc.
Peavey	Tool with sharp point and moveable cant hook to create leverage in moving logs.
Pecker pole	A small tree, often found in the understory of the old growth.
Peeler	Large logs suitable for rotary cutting against an 8-foot blade — a log grade suitable for producing veneers.
Pike pole	Long pole tipped with a spike and small hook for log sorting in river driving or in a holding pond.
Pioneer road	Rough preliminary road or bulldozer trail to allow movement of construction equipment.

Pistol grip	Tree with a curved butt usually caused by an earlier sideswipe from another tree.
Pit man	Man working with a power shovel or bulldozer who uses a hand shovel, swamps out or hooks mats.
Pole road	A trough made by parallel poles to form a skid road.
Pot	Old time donkey, often a one spooler.
Powder monkey	Man who handles dynamite and places the charges.
Prelog	Removal of small trees and/or windfalls before the primary logging of the main stand.
Pulaski	Heavy handled tool with oval eye used as a combination axe and hoe — (named after its originator).
Punk	Young logger, mostly used as a signal man e.g. whistle punk.
Push	Woods foreman or superintendent.
Quarter corner	Marker at half-mile intervals that divides a surveyed section of land into four parts.
Rack	Railroad car with bulkheads at either end used for loading wood products crosswise.
Reach	Timber or metal beam connecting a log truck with its trailer — also called a "stinger."
Rigging slinger	Head man on the rigging crew — rigs trees and changes the tail hold.
Rock powder	Dynamite with 60% purity for shooting rock.
Running line	Any wire rope that is moving during logging operations.
Saddle tank	Locomotive such as the Mallet where the water tank is mounted over the boiler.
Safety strap	A strap linking the bull block and a guy line so that a break would run down the guy line.

Scaler	One who measures log contents.
Schoolmarm	A log or tree that is forked — a stable log in river driving because it does not roll easily.
Scissorbill	Logger who contested the I.W.W. — later, any non-union man.
Second loader	Man who placed the tongs on logs for loading.
Selective logging	Removal of certain trees or small sections to allow for reseeding.
Set	A pair of fallers — originally a pair of buckers also.
Setting	The area to be logged to one spar tree — later the reach of a cat side.
Shake	A separation in a tree or log along the growth rings — common in spar trees as a result of yarding pressure.
Sheave	Flanged wheel that runs freely in a block i.e. pulley.
Sluice	Act of a log turn overrunning an animal team on a downhill pull.
Snag	Dead tree or stub left standing after logging.
Snatch block	Block which can be opened on one side to thread a line at any point.
Snipe	Rounding the leading edge of a log to keep it from digging in during yarding operations.
Snubber	Device for slowing down a moving turn — also a line used around a turn, donkey, etc. to slow it by friction.
Sougan	Heavy woolen blanket used by early loggers.
Spar tree	Tree large and tall enough to be used for yarding logs — sometimes raised in place by a block system.

Spark chaser	A handyman at a landing to put out small fires caused by the donkey.
Speeder	Powered railroad car for hauling men and supplies.
Spike	To fall a tree over a stump or rock, causing it to shatter.
Spot	Moving a car to be loaded into place — putting any equipment into a desired place.
Springboard	Short length of plank that fallers fit into the base of a tree to stand on.
Square lead	A yarding line directly out from the donkey drum.
Staghead	Refers to a tree with a dead top.
Staggered settings	Logging areas separated by standing trees.
Stranded line	Wire rope starting to separate from its hemp or wire core.
Sheer skid	Log or stump to guide logs around a corner — in the early days spools notched in stumps were used.
Shoo-fly	Construction road around a gully to move equipment — used extensively with trestle construction.
Short splice	A splice in wire rope that needs only modest strength, normally less than a foot long.
Show	Any logging operation.
Side	Refers to the crew on a logging operation.
Side rod	Foreman for one side — also assistant camp foreman.
Siwash tree	Tree left to deflect a running line.
Skid	In early logging the cross member used for roading logs — later, a reference to the act of yarding logs.

Skidder	Usually refers to a skyline system — can also be a yarder used on a hi-lead setting.
Skid road	Ground lead system using animals or donkey pot — old logging method utilizing greased skids.
Skinner	Ox, horse or mule driver, later applied to cat driver.
Skookum	Chinook jargon for something strong or well built.
Skyline	Yarding system where a tight line is run from a head spar to a back or tail spar, keeping the turn well up.
Slackline	Yarding system using a large drum to raise and lower a skyline (normally two inches in diameter).
Slack puller	One who pulls slack by hand — later adapted to power pulling by straw drum, etc.
Sleeper	Fire that appears out but later burns again — also refers to deferred blasting charge.
Straw drum	Auxiliary drum for the haywire or straw line.
Straw line	Small diameter wire rope — same as haywire line.
Stumper	Logger who lives at home and commutes to the job.
Swamper	One who clears out brush, etc. — in the early days it was the one that maintained and greased the skid roads.
Swede level	Level marker at grade foreman's eye height above the ground to determine when a cut is down to grade.
Sweep	Degree of curve in a log — also used in timbers.

Swing donkey	Yarder used to bring logs from a collection point to a landing — use of donkey to "swing" from a deck.
Tackle	Refers to the rigging blocks and swivels, etc.
Tail tree	See "Back spar" — used for the tail block.
Tommy Moore	A wide main block to allow the "jewelry" to pass through — used on a combination yarder and loader.
Top guy	One of the guy lines used at the top of a spar tree.
Tote road	A preliminary road on one designed only for hauling machinery and supplies.
Tower skidder	A skidder built with a steel tower mounted on a railroad car — commonly called a steel spar.
Trailing road	Old time skid road where a small locomotive is used for skidding logs down between the tracks.
Transfer line	Line to pull skidder lines to the side for a new yarding direction.
Tree jack	Triangular unit with three rollers to anchor the tail tree or tail hold of a sky-line.
Triple drum	Three drum system mounted on the rear of a cat to act as a yarder.
Turn	Logs brought in by chokers at one time.
Two speed	Yarding donkey with low speed for heavy hauling — derided by loggers as "slow and slower."
Undercut	Cutting a notch in a tree to determine the direction of fall — also cutting a log from the underside.
Wheel camp	Camp on railroad cars making it more portable — also called a "car camp."

Whistle punk	Starting job for loggers — one who signals the donkey engineer to go ahead, go ahead slow, etc.
Wickiup	Any temporary shelter to get out of the weather — sometimes used by animal drivers or a survey crew.
Widow maker	Any dangerous tree that could do in a faller — usually a loose limb or a leaning tree.
Windfall	Tree downed by the wind which is usually bucked and sometimes removed before falling the standing trees.
Wire axe	Old double-bitted axe driven into a stump so that a line can be cut on the exposed edge.
Wolf tree	A very limby tree that has grown out in the open.
Woodpecker	A small portable sawmill.
Wrapper	Chain or combination with wire rope to bind down a load of logs.
Yarding	Bringing in logs by any method.